Dealing with Foetal Alcohol Spectrum Disorder
A guide for social workers

Mary Mather

Published by
CoramBAAF Adoption and Fostering Academy
41 Brunswick Square
London WC1N 1AZ
www.corambaaf.org.uk

Coram Academy Limited, registered as a company limited by guarantee
in England and Wales number 9697712, part of the Coram group, charity
number 312278

British Library Cataloguing in Publication Data
A catalogue record for this book is available from the British Library

ISBN 978 1 910039 67 0

Project management by Jo Francis, CoramBAAF
Designed and typeset by Helen Joubert Design
Printed in Great Britain by the Lavenham Press

For the latest news on CoramBAAF titles and special offers, sign up to
our free publications bulletin at https://corambaaf.org.uk/subscribe.

Contents

Acknowledgements

I would like to acknowledge the invaluable contribution of the numerous parents, adopters, foster and kinship carers who have taught us so much about the daily realities of caring for children affected by exposure to prenatal alcohol. Thanks also to those who read a draft version of this document: Ellie Johnson, Health Group Development Officer, CoramBAAF; Marion Hundleby; Marjorie Morrison; Sharon Mulhern, senior practitioner, Cornerways Fostering Service; and Usha Sharma, social care consultant and trainer. Many thanks also to my grandchildren, George, John, Fred, Max, Emma, Eve, Zara, Harry, Meg and Joshua, who continue to teach me so much about child development.

Note about the author

Dr Mary Mather is a retired Consultant Community Paediatrician. She has been the medical adviser to three local authority adoption panels, a voluntary adoption agency and an intercountry adoption panel. She was an elected member of BAAF's (now CoramBAAF's) Health Advisory Group for 13 years and was the Chair of the Group from 2000–2005. She has lectured in the medical input to adoption and fostering as both a local and national speaker for 25 years. She has a particular interest in the long-term effects of drug and alcohol misuse in pregnancy and the impact of unrecognised prenatal exposure to alcohol in the difficulties experienced by both adopted and looked after children.

She has published 32 articles in peer-reviewed journals and co-authored the BAAF guidelines on the assessment of obesity and smoking in substitute carers. She is the author of *Doctors for Children in Public Care* (2000, BAAF) – the first UK textbook for medical advisers. She is the also co-author of *Parenting a Child with an Invisible Disability: The Foetal Alcohol Spectrum Disorders* (with Julia Brown, 2014, CreateSpace), a guide for parents and carers in the management of their children.

Preface

Throughout this book, the term Foetal Alcohol Spectrum Disorder (FASD) will be used. This is an umbrella term that is increasingly used to describe the whole range of lifelong permanent disabilities for a child that can result from a woman's use of alcohol during pregnancy.

Fetus, rather than foetus, is now the spelling used internationally. All the English-speaking countries of the world, all scientific publications and journals use this spelling, as does technical literature in the UK. However, the vast majority of UK organisations, support groups, social workers and parents still use the spelling foetus, which is why the decision was taken to use this spelling throughout the guide. When readers search online for information, much of which originates in the USA and Canada, or wish to access UK technical literature, it is important to spell the word fetus.

Although the situation is slowly improving, there are still many UK professionals in health, education and social services who have a poor awareness of, and a lack of training in, the complexity of this invisible disability. Too many parents are unable to get a diagnosis, and too many children are being diagnosed incorrectly and treated inappropriately. Lifelong support for the children and their families is still at a very early stage in the UK.

Increased professional knowledge and better understanding are the keys to successful future management. This guide is intended to provide information for all those who care for children affected by prenatal alcohol and help them to understand and respond correctly to their problems.

The information is valid throughout the UK and is particularly directed at social care, emphasising the vital role social workers should play in the diagnosis.

Chapter 1
Our continuing love affair with alcohol

Here's to alcohol, the cause of and the solution to all life's problems.

(Homer Simpson, *The Simpsons*)

IN THE BEGINNING...

There is nothing new about the issue of alcohol; the pleasures and problems that it brings have been with us for a very long time. Alcoholic drinks have been produced and consumed by humans for thousands of years. Alcohol has medicinal, antiseptic and analgesic properties. Alcoholic drinks encourage relaxation and social cohesion and have played a significant role in religion. However, the role of alcoholic drinks in society has often been highly controversial and the subject of great debate. The contradiction between alcohol as essential for pleasure and drunkenness as a social evil is found throughout world history.

Archaeological evidence suggests that as long ago as 10,000 BC, our Neolithic ancestors fermented and drank beer. Tools to produce wine, dating back to 7,000 BC, have been discovered in China. By 4,000 BC, wine had started to appear in Egyptian pictographs. The ancient Greeks wrote at length about the positive and negative effects of alcohol and many of the great philosophers had strong opinions on the subject. Plato, for example, believed, 'He was a wise man who invented beer'. He and his contemporaries were, however, strongly critical of drunkenness.

During the time of the Romans, the trade in wine and other alcoholic beverages grew rapidly across the Empire. Every villa had its own vineyard. The Roman philosopher Seneca stated that, 'Drunkenness is nothing but voluntary madness'. Alcohol was distributed free, or at cost, for festivals and victory celebrations and frequently led to large-scale disorder and riots.

Modern European drinking habits still reflect the pattern established nearly 2,000 years ago by the Greeks and Romans. Wine drinking in moderation, usually with meals, still predominates in the south of Europe. In the north of Europe, where vines could not easily be cultivated, beer drinking, without accompanying food, is more common. The beer drinking countries – Germany, Austria, Belgium, Denmark, the Czech Republic, Britain and Ireland – would, however, be regarded as semi-barbarian territory by the Romans. Thanks to the Romans, wine is still regarded as the most civilised and cultured of drinks. Wine not beer is still the drink served to impress at banquets, political summits and dinner parties because of its enduring association with class, status and wealth (Standage, 2005).

THROUGH THE AGES

By the end of the Middle Ages, most European nations had developed their own distinctive brewing and distilling styles. In Europe, religious orders have had a large part to play in the history of alcohol. It was monks who first perfected brewing and the large-scale production of beers and wines, which they would sell to the public. Religious orders of the time successfully managed the paradox of simultaneously regarding alcohol as a gift from God whilst at the same time condemning drunkenness as a sin.

The issue of excessive alcohol consumption in the UK has been an issue in debates about public health and social morals for over 300 years. The large-scale distillation of alcohol from grain into spirits, often flavoured with juniper, became immensely popular during this time. In 1690, the English Parliament even passed a law to encourage 'the Distillation of Brandy and Spirits from Corn'. This led to a massive surge in gin production and consumption, which was quickly blamed for widespread health problems and social unrest. Hogarth's print, *Gin Lane*, published in 1751, painted a graphic picture of the social disorder that followed the availability of cheap gin. Concern over the effects of gin on society led to the Gin Acts, of 1736 and 1751 respectively, which taxed and regulated the production and sale of gin. Distilled spirits, particularly rum, were also the currency that fuelled and closed the malevolent triangle of the slave trade, linking spirits, slaves and sugar.

The problems escalated as British cities grew rapidly during the industrial revolution. In the early 18th century, the mortality rate from gin was thought to be so high that it stabilised London's rapidly growing population. Temperance movements mushroomed around the 1860s in response to public concern, fuelled by the teachings of evangelistic religion and social reformers like Joseph Rowntree.

Distilled drinks, alongside firearms and infectious disease, helped to shape the modern world, as the inhabitants of the Old World sought to establish themselves as rulers of the New. Alcohol played a role in the enslavement and displacement of millions of people from indigenous cultures who were supplied by copious quantities of alcohol in exchange for goods or land. Today, this association with slavery and exploitation has gone but the damage persists. The highest prevalence of foetal alcohol spectrum disorders in the world are found in the indigenous populations of Australia, New Zealand, Canada and the USA. Alcohol has always provided an escape from poverty and hardship, an association that endures.

History also suggests that banning the sale of alcohol does not decrease consumption but simply encourages the growth of a black market in illicit and more dangerous formulas. In the USA in the 19th century, spirits were produced and consumed in almost unbelievable quantities. By the 1820s, a surplus of corn had led to a massive growth in the production of whisky. It is thought that during this time, the equivalent of a pint of whisky for every man, woman and child was being drunk every day across America. This led to the beginning of the Prohibition movement, which sought to ban all forms of alcohol across the USA. Prohibition reached its climax with the National Prohibition Act in 1919, which led to the banning of the sale and manufacture of alcohol across the USA between 1920 and 1933. Owing to the massively lucrative trade in black market alcohol that followed, Prohibition is widely regarded as having done more to boost organised crime than any other Act in the history of the USA.

MORE RECENTLY...

In the UK, the late 20th and early 21st centuries have seen widespread increases in public drunkenness. UK society has a particularly close relationship with alcohol; it is central to most of our rituals, such as weddings, christenings, funerals, leaving parties, stag nights and hen nights, and even our everyday life. The ubiquitous teapot on the dining tables of post-war Britain has been steadily replaced by the wine bottle. For most people, drinking alcohol is associated with socialising and pleasurable experiences. Responsible drinking is all about understanding the harm alcohol can have on your health, both mentally and physically, if not consumed with care and moderation. Despite numerous public health campaigns, a substantial number of drinkers regularly consume more than the recommended weekly guidelines, because they lack sufficient understanding of the harm alcohol can have and frequently cannot make sense of the confusing unit system by which alcohol strength is measured.

In modern-day UK, there is still a conflict of views as to whether alcohol is an attractive elixir or a dangerous poison. It has been accepted for two hundred years that alcohol can have a negative impact on family life, leading to domestic violence and the neglect of children. During two World Wars, successive Governments were concerned about the deleterious impact of alcohol on industrial production because of the country's need for a punctual, sober, reliable workforce. More recently, the debate has focused on the cost to individuals and society of premature illness and death and the impact on NHS, police and community resources.

There is, however, one important group in society for whom alcohol will always be a poison and that is the unborn child. The unborn child has not been a part of 2,000 years of debate. The damage that prenatal alcohol causes to the developing foetal brain will be the focus of this guide.

KEY LEARNING POINT

- Whatever the benefits and disadvantages of alcohol to society, for the unborn child it is always a dangerous poison that must be avoided.

Chapter 2
The unpredictable impact of alcohol on the developing foetus

[Alcohol is] too often the cause of weak and feeble, distempered children.

(Royal College of Physicians, London, 1725)

The adverse effects of alcohol in human pregnancy were not systematically studied until the 1970s, although negative effects have been sporadically noted throughout history, dating back even to the Bible.

In the Book of Judges, an angel appears to the mother of Samson saying: 'Behold, thou shalt conceive, and bear a son; and now drink no wine nor strong drink, neither eat any unclean thing' (Judges 13:7). In ancient Carthage, there was reported to be a prohibition against couples drinking on their wedding night to prevent them producing an affected offspring. In 1725, at the height of London's gin epidemic, the College of Physicians in London warned the House of Commons that alcohol is 'too often the cause of weak and feeble, distempered children'. In 1837, Charles Dickens, writing in *The Pickwick Papers*, describes Betsy Martin:

Widow, one child, and one eye. Goes out charing and washing, by the day; never had more than one eye, but knows her mother drank bottled stout, and shouldn't wonder if that caused it. Thinks it not impossible that if she had always abstained from spirits she might have had two eyes by this time.

EARLIER STUDIES

The first scientific study of children of alcoholic mothers was conducted in 1899 by a British physician, William Sullivan, working in a Liverpool prison. Dr Sullivan observed 600 children born to 120 alcoholic mothers and compared them to the children of their non-drinking blood relatives. He found a stillbirth and infant death rate of 56 per cent compared to 24 per cent in their abstinent relatives. He also found that the problems in the foetus increased with the mother's alcohol intake.

A more important aspect to Sullivan's paper was his case study of 11 alcoholic mothers who were forced to abstain from alcohol during pregnancy because of their imprisonment. Among these mothers, Sullivan found that the mothers who entered prison in early pregnancy had healthier babies and a decreased infant mortality compared to their siblings born before their mothers went to prison.

Although Sullivan's findings were suggestive of a direct toxic effect of alcohol on the foetus, and subsequent animal studies suggested the same, the moral undertones of the temperance movement in the USA created a climate where alcoholism research was considered by many as moralistic and unscientific. The subject was largely ignored for a further 50 years.

In 1968, Paul Lemoine, a physician in Paris, published a clinical description of 127 children of alcoholic mothers. His descriptions of physical malformations, developmental delays and behavioural challenges were one of the first descriptions of the impact of alcohol on the developing foetus. Jones and Smith, writing in the *Lancet* in 1973, described similar problems in infants in a Seattle hospital and formally used the term "foetal alcohol syndrome" (FAS) for the first time.

Research on the neurodevelopmental effects of prenatal alcohol exposure exploded in the 1970s and has now continued for nearly 50 years. To highlight the scale of this research, a search for "foetal alcohol syndrome" in PubMed (an archive of worldwide medical publications), showed that between 1950 and 1972 there were no publications on this subject but since then there has been an average of 15,000–20,000 publications per year. In 2016, for example, there were 16,357 articles. Initially, the bulk of this research was done in the USA and Canada and alcohol is now the subject of research in most developed countries. However, the UK still lags behind the rest of the world. There is still a great reluctance here to accept the growing international consensus about the negative impact of alcohol on foetal development.

Given its complexity, many things influence brain development, so how do we know that it is the alcohol that causes the cognitive, emotional and social difficulties associated with FASD, and not the other disadvantages suffered by individuals who are dependent on alcohol? Many children born to parents who are affected by alcohol or drug abuse have poor lifestyles and diets and suffer neglectful parenting. Professionals often argue that it is these factors that are the cause of all, or most, of the symptoms of FASD. Rigorous scientific studies have now dealt very convincingly with this debate. Numerous studies across the world have shown very clearly that it is exposure to alcohol in the early stages of brain development that causes enduring and permanent brain damage, irrespective of the environment in which the child grows up.

WHAT MODERN DAY PRENATAL ALCOHOL RESEARCH HAS SHOWN

In a short practice guide, it would not be practical to reference and document the enormous amount of human and animal research that has been done over the last 50 years. As very few professionals need to have detailed scientific knowledge of the neuroanatomy of the developing foetus, the following is a summary of what the last 50 years has revealed. Further reading and references for those interested in this subject are listed in the references (see Lemoine *et al*, 1968; Jones and Smith, 1973; Warner and Rosett, 1975; Streissguth *et al*, 1980; Stratton *et al*, 1996; Mattson *et al*, 2001; Preece and Riley, 2011; Sullivan, 2011; and Phillips, 2015).

Firstly, it is absolutely essential to recognise that 50 years of detailed scientific research has established beyond doubt that alcohol can damage every cell in the developing foetus but has a particularly severe impact on the developing brain structure and function. The resulting physical and mental problems vary in severity but are permanent and lifelong.

Alcohol disrupts cellular function and development

Alcohol is a teratogen, or poison. A teratogen is any substance that disrupts the development of a foetus and causes birth defects. The teratogen that is best known to the general public is thalidomide, which was marketed in the 1950s as a mild sleeping pill safe even for pregnant women. However, it caused thousands of babies worldwide to be born with malformed limbs. Alcohol affects developing cells in many ways, causing cellular damage, disorganisation, dysfunction and even cell death. It disrupts the mitochondrial system within cells that are responsible for energy production. Alcohol interferes with growth factors necessary for normal development and the maintenance of cellular function. It interferes with the chemical transmitters that pass information between cells.

Alcohol is a potent neurotoxin

The impact of alcohol is particularly serious for the developing brain and spinal cord. The cells in the brain and spinal cord have a lower threshold for alcohol exposure and experience more rapid cell death than other cells in the body. Whereas the other major organs develop in the first three months, the central nervous system continues to develop throughout pregnancy and remains vulnerable for the full nine months of gestation.

Within the foetus, the embryonic cells destined to become brain neurons grow in number, move to their ultimate locations, and then mature into a wide variety of functionally distinct neuronal cell types, eventually forming connections with other brain cells in a predetermined pattern. Under the influence of alcohol, this process is disrupted. The developing neurons may be unable to migrate to their proper location and some neurons end up in the wrong part of the brain. Alcohol appears to delay the development of the neurotransmitter systems, particularly serotonin. Without serotonin, normal brain development does not occur. Microcephaly (a small head) due to deficient brain growth, and other structural brain abnormalities occur.

The overall reduction in brain size is most marked in the parietal and frontal lobes. The frontal lobe of the brain controls important cognitive skills in humans, such as emotional expression, problem solving, memory, language, judgement, and sexual behaviour. It can be thought of as the "control panel" of both our personality and our ability to communicate. The parietal lobe is where sensory information such as taste, temperature and touch are integrated and processed. This damage is later manifested in behaviour that is perceived to be immature and inappropriate.

The influence of alcohol results in reductions in the amount of white matter throughout the brain. White matter transmits information quickly because of its electrically insulating **myelin** sheaths. It is the essential communications network of the brain that connects different regions to each another and allows information to pass quickly between them. Inadequate white matter means that information is only processed slowly. Affected individuals have longer reaction times because they only process information slowly and inefficiently. Individual differences in intelligence are based in part on how quickly the brain processes information.

Prenatal alcohol exposure is one of the major causes of impaired development, or complete absence of the corpus callosum. Approximately seven per cent of children with FAS may lack a corpus callosum, an incidence rate 20 times higher than that in the general population. Humans have two cerebral hemispheres in the brain. The left side of the brain controls concrete ideas, practical details, orderly sequences, our understanding of rules, and predicting the consequences of our actions. The right side of the brain controls abstract thinking, emotions and feelings, creativity, and intuition. The corpus callosum is a bundle of about 200 million axons that connects these two sides of the brain and is the major communication link between the right and left cerebral hemispheres. The primary function of the corpus callosum is to integrate motor, sensory and cognitive performances between the cerebral cortex on one side of the brain with the same region on the other side. When the corpus callosum is damaged or does not function adequately, there are not as many pathways between the two sides of the brain and information is only passed slowly and inefficiently. This may account in part for why, when a child with FAS has an impulse to do something, the action happens first, and the consequences are only realised later.

Prenatal alcohol exposure can also lead to reductions in the size of the cerebellum and the basal ganglia. These structures are important for spatial memory, movement, co-ordination, posture and balance. When they are damaged, the ability to perform everyday tasks is impaired, as is the ability to shift attention from one task to another. These structures are also essential to being able to stay balanced and upright. Individuals who have suffered damage to the cerebellum struggle with keeping their balance and maintaining proper muscle co-ordination.

Other effects

Increases in stillbirths and infant mortality have been confirmed among mothers who drink heavily or binge while pregnant. Heavy drinking (defined as one or more drinks per day in pregnancy) doubles the risk of a pre-term birth. Drinking in the first three months of pregnancy also increases the risks of miscarriage, premature delivery and low birth weight. Three or more drinks per week doubles the risk of low birth weight. Women who drink heavily also tend to smoke, a factor that increases the risk of low birth weight.

Alcohol impairs and damages the growth of all cells, and other organs in the body can also be affected. Congenital heart defects are common. Structural defects have been reported in the liver and kidneys, as have defects in the skeleton and eyes. The characteristic facial features of children with FAS, due to impaired growth of the developing face, will be described in the next chapter on diagnosis.

However, for the affected individual the main impact of exposure to alcohol is not physical but behavioural. The life-changing consequences of heavy prenatal alcohol exposure are deficits in intellectual ability, reduced attention, reduced speed of information processing, deficits in executive functioning, language, visual perception, learning and memory. When these problems occur without any other diagnostic features, alcohol exposure is frequently forgotten or considered irrelevant.

CAN DRINKING ALCOHOL IN PREGNANCY EVER BE CONSIDERED "SAFE"?

Although the risk is higher with heavy alcohol use, any amount of alcohol can affect the developing foetus. There is no evidence of a "safe" drinking level in pregnancy. As the amount of alcohol consumed by the mother increases, so does the amount of damage inflicted on the foetus. The impact will also depend on the pattern of the mother's drinking. A single drink once a week spaced over several hours will have a different effect on the foetus than drinking substantial amounts over small periods of time, or drinking constantly for several days. The degree of damage to the unborn baby will depend on the stage of development, because different parts of the body and brain develop at different times during pregnancy. Each affected child therefore has an individual and very unique pattern of strengths and difficulties.

The effects that alcohol has on a developing foetus also depend on whether the mother uses other drugs, smokes or has poor health during pregnancy. In these cases, her child is more likely to have problems. There may also be a genetic link because some babies are more likely to be harmed by alcohol than others.

Advising any pregnant woman about taking medication in pregnancy is a delicate balance between risk and benefit. The balance in relation to alcohol falls clearly on the side of risk. Alcohol is not essential to the health or well-being of a pregnant woman and is known to be teratogenic to her baby. Alcohol is not a drug that a doctor would ever "prescribe" in pregnancy and it is not a drug that should ever be advised, even in small doses (Mather *et al*, 2015).

KEY LEARNING POINT

- The damage that alcohol does to the developing foetus, particularly the developing brain, has been conclusively proved by over 50 years of rigorous scientific research. It is permanent and lifelong but totally preventable.

Chapter 3
Drinking alcohol in pregnancy in the 21st century

Giving up alcohol makes me very stressed and surely stress is much worse for the baby than a glass of wine.

(29-year-old journalist, five months pregnant)

I am 39, accustomed to having a casual drink with lunch or dinner and unwilling to give it up. My grandmother and mother drank and smoked and I'm fine. Doctors have been wrong before.

(Senior social work manager)

THE GLOBAL PICTURE

Prenatal exposure to alcohol is now accepted as the commonest and most preventable cause of mental retardation in the world. In every country where women drink in pregnancy, children are being born with FASD. Despite strenuous public health campaigns, in most countries women continue to drink in pregnancy. The incidence of FASD in a country mirrors the consumption of alcohol and the prevalence of alcohol misuse.

A new study published in 2017 in *The Lancet Global Health* (Popova *et al*) estimated that globally about 10 per cent of women drink in pregnancy and one in every 67 women who consumes alcohol in pregnancy will deliver a child with FAS. This means that globally, on average, 119,000 children with FAS are born every year. The cost to society, as well as to the individuals and their families, is staggering.

The same study also found that the UK has one of the worst rates of drinking in pregnancy in the European region, with only Ireland, Denmark and Belarus showing higher figures. The estimated prevalence of alcohol use in pregnancy is highest in Russia, the UK, Denmark, Belarus and Ireland. The lowest prevalence is in Oman, Kuwait, the United Arab Emirates, Saudi Arabia and Qatar; all predominantly Muslim countries, a religion that is associated with high rates of abstinence from alcohol. However, the risk exists for any child. Although some parts of the world have a lower risk, the sad fact is that any child from any country in the world could have been exposed to alcohol prenatally.

In the USA, the Surgeon General first advised women not to drink in pregnancy as early as 1981. Over the next 20 years, the same guidance was given to pregnant women in Canada, Denmark, France, Norway, Israel, Mexico, Australia, Ireland, New Zealand, Spain, the Netherlands and Scotland. Current USA guidance from the Surgeon General (2005) clearly states: 'There is no known safe amount of alcohol to drink while pregnant, no safe time to drink and no safe kind of alcohol'.

FIFTY YEARS OF CONFUSING UK GUIDANCE

For over 50 years, the advice given to UK women by professionals has been a contradictory, confusing barrage of mixed messages. During this period, no advisory body in England and Wales gave a clear recommendation to abstain from alcohol in pregnancy. The Department of Health recommended that pregnant women should avoid alcohol, but undermined that advice by then giving an apparently "safe" level for alcohol in pregnancy, saying that if a woman "chooses to drink", she should drink no more than four units per week (Mather, 2015). The National Institute for Health and Care Excellence (NICE) emphasised the importance of avoiding alcohol in the first three months of pregnancy due to an association with miscarriage. The Royal College of Obstetricians and Gynaecologists stated that small amounts of alcohol had not been shown to be harmful. This advice was given even though very few pregnant women, or professionals, understood the concept of a "unit" of alcohol (Mukherjee *et al*, 2013), and that the phrase "choose to drink" was open to misinterpretation. It was 2016 before the UK finally joined the growing international consensus that all alcohol should be avoided during pregnancy.

The current guidance, issued in January 2016 by the Chief Medical Officer for England, Wales, Scotland and Northern Ireland, is that if you are pregnant or planning to become pregnant, the safest approach is not to drink alcohol at all to keep risks to your baby to a minimum. Drinking in pregnancy can lead to long-term harm to the baby, with the more you drink, the greater the risk.

This advice has not yet reached a significant number of UK pregnant women, who continue drinking in pregnancy to a level that puts their babies at risk. A recent UK prospective study in Leeds (Nykjaer *et al*, 2014) showed that the proportion of women drinking alcohol during pregnancy was 79 per cent, 63 per cent and 49 per cent for the first, second and third trimesters respectively. Few of these women were considered to be problem drinkers.

More worryingly, there is growing evidence of a link between higher education, higher socioeconomic status and excessive alcohol consumption, which is notably strong in UK women. The same Leeds study showed that the pregnant woman most likely to drink was over 35, in a managerial or professional occupation and from a white ethnic background. These are highly educated women who, despite the scientific evidence, continue to believe that drinking alcohol poses no risks to their unborn child.

At the time of writing, there are no UK population prevalence data for either alcohol use in pregnancy or FAS. Worldwide estimates are that at least one per cent of live births are affected by prenatal alcohol and alcohol is the leading preventable cause of birth defects, and developmental and learning disability. Accepting that this one per cent figure also applies to the UK, this means that at least 7,000 babies affected by alcohol will be born every year in the UK. This is more than the combined total number of infants with Down's Syndrome, cerebral palsy, cystic fibrosis, spina bifida and Sudden Infant Death Syndrome (SIDS). However, given the social importance of alcohol to UK society, this one per cent figure is generally thought to be an underestimate and most experts would agree that a figure closer to three per cent or even five per cent is much more likely to be accurate.

Even more concerning are the pregnant women who are chronically dependent on alcohol and/or drugs and whose children will be subject to state intervention in their lives. These children will face the complexities of life as a looked after child with the added burden that their disabilities due to alcohol are often unrecognised. These children pose a huge challenge to all our services. There is an urgent need to recognise prenatal alcohol exposure at an early stage and to develop pathways for diagnosis, assessment and support for affected children.

Why is it that despite all that is now known about alcohol, health and social care professionals are still not particularly well informed in this area? In contrast to other developed countries, in the UK there is still widespread denial of the importance of the problem. The UK has a relatively light touch system of regulation compared to many developed countries. Only in Scotland has the Government attempted to make cheap alcohol less available through a ban on multi-buy promotions and plans to introduce a minimum price per unit of alcohol. Liberalising the licensing laws has led to intense competition among retailers, driving down supermarket prices and shifting alcohol consumption away from pubs into the home. It is much cheaper to buy alcohol by the bottle in a shop than by the glass in a bar. Major sporting events are supported by generous alcohol sponsorship and the link between alcohol and sport, both on and off the pitch, is ingrained in the British psyche. The UK, except for Scotland, is the only EU member apart from Malta to maintain a drink driving blood alcohol limit of 80mgs. Advertising has also progressively targeted women, particularly young women, with fruit-based beers and ciders and drinks marketed as low calorie. Wine and vodka, drinks generally preferred by women, have reduced in price in real terms. The result is a regulatory system that totally fails to protect the vulnerable and children.

KEY LEARNING POINT

- As many as 119,000 children may be born with FAS globally every year. In the UK, alcohol damage could affect between one–five per cent of pregnancies. The lower figure (one per cent) means that 7,000 affected children are born every year. The costs to the children, their families and society are staggering.

Chapter 4

Working with pregnant women to prevent alcohol damage

If you could prevent brain damage in an unborn child, would you?

(Sir Al Aynsley-Green, first Children's Commissioner for England 2005–10, Professor Emeritus of Child Health, University College London)

The goal for all professionals working with pregnant women and their unborn children must be to prevent any alcohol damage. Successful prevention strategies should target all women of childbearing age. All pregnant women should be routinely screened for alcohol misuse. This means the development of universal strategies aimed at everybody, plus selective strategies for women at high risk.

A comprehensive range of prevention services does not currently exist in the UK. Services are patchy and the situation can be challenging for any professional working with a pregnant woman. In the absence of a comprehensive national strategy, all professionals should individually try to reduce the number of damaged children in our society by:

- working towards a UK-wide universal prevention strategy – a model is detailed below;

- increasing their own personal knowledge;

- learning how to sensitively talk about alcohol with a pregnant woman;

- understanding the unit system and how to record alcohol consumption accurately.

A MODEL UNIVERSAL PREVENTION STRATEGY

The prevention of FASD requires a national, co-ordinated, multi-faceted approach. A good example is the holistic approach that has developed over the past decade in Canada, which incorporates the following levels.

Level 1: Increasing awareness and public education

The first level involves strategies aimed at the general population that raise public awareness, such as educational campaigns, the involvement of schools, warning posters, and the use of the media. Training programmes for healthcare professionals and those working in the fields of social work, criminal justice and education, on the prevention, diagnosis and management of the range of FASD are implemented.

Level 2: Discussion of alcohol use with all women of childbearing years and their support networks

The second level of prevention involves discussing with all women of childbearing years and their support networks, alcohol use, the risks of drinking alcohol, coping without alcohol, the prenatal supports available, and pregnancy planning. Leaflets appropriate to a UK population can be obtained from all the FAS charities (listed in Appendix C) and many local authorities and health care trusts. A significant aspect of the Canadian approach to prevention is that advice on alcohol consumption is provided not only to women of childbearing years, but also to their wider support network, including their partners and close family. This underlines the importance of creating a supportive environment for not drinking throughout pregnancy, and recognises that the prevention is a collective family and professional responsibility.

Level 3: Specialised, holistic support of pregnant women with alcohol and other health and social problems

The third level is delivered through specialised, holistic support of pregnant women with substance misuse, health and or social problems. Critical to this is a culturally relevant, non-judgemental approach, with accessible and comprehensive services helping to reduce barriers to care. Evaluations of Level 3 prevention services show that women who access these services experience improvements in physical health, nutritional status, housing, access to substance use treatment, parenting capacity and ability to retain custody of their children (Alberta Alcohol and Drug Abuse Commission, 2006; Motz *et al*, 2006).

Level 4: Postpartum support for new mothers assisting them to maintain/initiate changes in their health and social networks and to support the development of their children

The fourth level involves supporting new mothers to maintain healthy changes in their alcohol use, and providing postpartum support for those mothers who were not able to make significant changes in their substance use. This stage may also involve early intervention services for their children.

TALKING SENSITIVELY TO A PREGNANT WOMAN ABOUT ALCOHOL

Pregnant women are generally motivated to change their behaviour and only rarely have severe alcohol problems. Every pregnant woman should be asked about her alcohol consumption in the context of a general discussion about her health, diet and support. The following format can be useful.

Discussing her reasons for drinking

This will be different for every woman.

- Her partner and family may be absent or unsupportive.

- Her family's lifestyle may involve a culture of heavy drinking and she is under social pressure to drink.

- She may be confused by mixed messages coming from her relatives, the media or even health professionals.

- She may have co-existing mental health problems, especially anxiety and depression that are often associated with excess alcohol consumption.

- She may be unaware of the damage that alcohol can do to her baby or may even think that alcohol has some positive benefits, for example, it is a source of iron.

- She may fear that her child will be taken away if she admits that she is drinking.

To prevent anaemia, a pregnant woman needs to increase the iron content of her diet to about 27mgs per day. In the past, a well-known stout, widely advertised as "good for you", was often recommended in pregnancy and during breastfeeding as a source of additional iron. However, a pint of stout contains 2.3 units of alcohol and only 0.1mg of iron. A woman could get the same amount of iron by eating 15 peas! In comparison, a single boiled egg contains 1.2mgs of iron, as well as protein, fat, vitamins and minerals, and poses absolutely no risk to a baby.

Asking difficult questions and making brief interventions

Most women will accept help if they are not made to feel guilty and are sure that it is safe to be honest. No woman wants to harm her baby intentionally and all women want to have a healthy baby. Professionals must avoid being judgemental and should always focus on these natural instincts.

Maternal alcohol consumption is normally self-reported and often underestimated. The statement "1–2 units once or twice per week", which is universally documented in both health and social work records, means virtually nothing. Frequently, neither the patient nor the professional understands what a unit is, but it is a socially acceptable response to the ill-advised single, open-ended question 'How much do you drink?' Targeted questions, with the aim of identifying the woman at high risk, are much more likely to yield a meaningful response. For example:

● What do you know about alcohol in pregnancy?

● Would you like more information about this?

● Were you drinking alcohol before you became pregnant?

● Are you drinking alcohol now?

● Do you find it difficult to relax and enjoy yourself without having a drink?

● When did you last have an alcoholic drink?

● How many drinks did you have on that occasion?

● Can you talk me through what you normally drink in a week and on your heaviest drinking day during the week?

● Would you find it difficult to give up alcohol whilst you are pregnant?

● Would you like any extra support to do this?

"Brief interventions" like this have been demonstrated to be a low-cost, effective use of professional resources. They take very little time and are based on research showing that people benefit from being given appropriate information at the right time. They are usually conducted in a one-to-one situation and can be implemented anywhere. The interventions are brief and "opportunistic", and can last as little as 30 seconds. They involve listening, giving advice, provoking further thought and may include the provision of self-help material. They are non-confrontational and non-judgemental, making the most of a brief opportunity to raise awareness, share knowledge and get a person thinking about making changes that will improve their health and reduce risky behaviour.

In alcohol misuse, a successful brief intervention will motivate a person to look at their drinking pattern and will then support them in reducing the risk to their health. This option works particularly well for women who are less likely to engage in counselling sessions or formal appointments and those who may be more impulsive and erratic in their decision-making. They are most effective in women who have family support. They can be even more effective when the woman's partner or family members share in the discussion. They are not suitable for women who are alcohol dependent. A model for a brief intervention developed by NHS Scotland can be found in Appendix A.

Whilst global messages, such as billboard posters, have been shown to have a very limited effect on behaviour, targeted interventions, such as leaflets from a midwife or brief interventions from a practitioner, can all lead to significant levels of reduction in drinking during pregnancy (Mukherjee *et al*, 2017).

IDENTIFYING THE HIGH-RISK PREGNANCY

It is essential, however, that the high-risk pregnancy, in a woman who is unable to stop drinking, is recognised as early as possible to reduce the risks to the developing foetus. People with alcohol and drug problems and their families are also vulnerable to other risks and the following factors should all raise concerns about the possibility of co-existent alcohol damage.

- A family history of alcohol misuse. Alcohol dependence often runs in families. This is partially a genetic effect, but is also influenced by a family's attitudes to alcohol that determine the environment in which a child has grown up.

- Suicide and self-harm are much greater in people with drink problems.

- Alcohol impairs parenting capacity; neglect can be secondary to alcohol dependence.

- There is a strong association between domestic violence and alcohol dependence.

- Having had a previous child removed because of alcohol-related problems.

In the families with multiple problems, who are more likely to come to the attention of the social worker, brief interventions are unlikely to be successful. A different type of intervention is needed. It is essential that a more structured approach is taken in these cases to assessing the potential danger to the developing foetus. This approach requires professionals who can accurately assess the amount of alcohol a woman is drinking and who have a knowledge of both the unit system and the use of structured questionnaires. These two topics will be considered in detail in the next chapter.

However, before this, it is important to appreciate that social workers should never advise a woman who drinks heavily to just stop drinking, because sudden withdrawal can cause a serious reaction. Alcohol withdrawal symptoms start within 6 to 12 hours after a woman suddenly stops drinking. The symptoms include tachycardia (a rapid pulse rate), hypertension, nausea, vomiting, agitation, hallucinations and grand mal seizures. In pregnancy, these withdrawal symptoms are associated with adverse complications for the foetus such as premature labour. Women identified to have heavy drinking patterns and who are unlikely to reduce their consumption should be referred for professional alcohol treatment. The detoxification of an alcohol-dependent pregnant woman should always be considered in an inpatient setting.

KEY LEARNING POINT

- The advice provided by professionals should be up to date, consistent and evidence-based. Pregnant women are vulnerable and need empathetic, non-judgemental care. No matter what the stage of her pregnancy, her baby will always benefit when she stops drinking.

Chapter 5
What is a unit and the use of structured questionnaires

Alcohol units: 5: Drowning sorrows. Cigarettes: 23: Fumigating sorrows. Calories: 3,856. Smothering sorrows in fat duvet.

(Helen Fielding, *Bridget Jones's Diary*)

WHAT IS A UNIT?

Alcohol consumption is measured in units. In the UK, one unit is 10ml of pure alcohol. Research has shown that when people are helped to count how many units they drink, it will not only help them to cut down but can also help the professional to assess the severity of their alcohol problems. The difficulty is that very few people in the general population, including most professionals, understand this system. The most common misassumption is that one unit is one drink of any kind, usually the type they themselves drink!

What does one unit of alcohol look like?

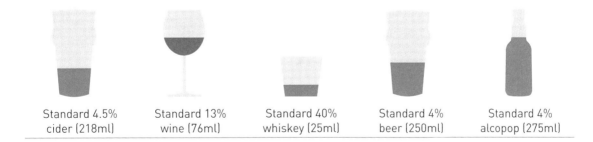

| Standard 4.5% cider (218ml) | Standard 13% wine (76ml) | Standard 40% whiskey (25ml) | Standard 4% beer (250ml) | Standard 4% alcopop (275ml) |

(Image adapted from Drinkaware information)

Note that one unit of 13 per cent wine is only 76mls; a small glass in a pub is 175mls.

The UK Chief Medical Officer issued the following guidelines for both men and women in August 2016:

- *To keep health risks from alcohol to a low level, it is safest not to drink more than 14 units a week on a regular basis.*

- *If you regularly drink as much as 14 units per week, it's best to spread your drinking evenly over three or more days. If you have one or two heavy drinking episodes a week, you increase your risk of death from long-term illness and injuries.*

- *The risk of developing a range of health problems (including cancers of the mouth, throat and breast) increases the more you drink on a regular basis.*

- *To cut down the amount you drink, a good way to help achieve this is to have several drink-free days a week.*

(Department of Health *et al*, 2016)

This is what 14 units of alcohol looks like:

This means you should not drink more than this amount of wine...

175ml glasses of 13% wine

OR this amount of lager or ale

568ml pints of 4% lager or ale

OR this amount of cider

568ml pints of 4.5% cider

OR this amount of spirits

25ml glasses of 40% spirits

(Image adapted from Drinkaware information)

The number of units is influenced by the strength of the alcohol that is drunk and the size of the glass.

In the two images shown above, the strength of the wine is assumed to be 13 per cent alcohol. The strength of white wine varies between eight per cent for sweet wines to 14 per cent for dry wine. Red wine varies between 12–15 per cent alcohol. At 14 per cent alcohol, 14 units is only five glasses (175ml) of wine. The strength of the beer in the above images is four per cent alcohol. Beers range in strength from three-and-a-half per cent to nine per cent for some artisan and extra-strength beers. At 5.2 per cent alcohol, 14 units is only four pints of beer.

14 units of higher strength beer or wine looks like this:

How much alcohol is there in a standard drink?

1 unit contains 10ml or 8g of alcohol

14 units (UK guidance per week for men and women) is equivalent to 4 pints of high strength beer or 5 large glasses of 14% wine (see below)

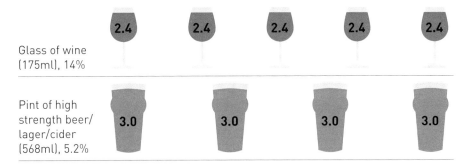

Glass of wine (175ml), 14%

Pint of high strength beer/ lager/cider (568ml), 5.2%

(Image adapted from Drinkaware information)

The size of the glass also makes a difference. The standard one unit of alcohol is based on a 125ml wine glass. Apart from champagne, most licensed retailers sell wine in 175ml glasses, which is a pub "small" glass, or 250ml glasses, which is a pub "large" glass. Frequently, it is relatively cheaper to buy the larger glass, or even the whole bottle, rather than the smaller one. Two large glasses of 14 per cent wine in a pub is nearly a pint of wine and six units of alcohol. For more information on calculating the units in alcoholic drinks, see the resources listed in Appendix D.

The number of units you are drinking depends on the size and strength of your drink

11% ABV wine		14% ABV wine	2.8% ABV lager		4.8% ABV lager
1.4 units		**1.8** units	**0.8** units		**1.4** units
	125ml glass			284ml half pint	
1.9 units		**2.5** units	**1.2** units		**2.1** units
	175ml glass			440ml can	
2.8 units		**3.5** units	**1.6** units		**2.7** units
	250ml glass			568ml pint	
8.3 units		**10.5** units	**1.8** units		**3.2** units
	750ml bottle			660ml bottle	

(© Crown copyright 2016
Image taken from Department of Health *et al*, 2016)

In the UK, there is no nationally agreed definition of what constitutes heavy or binge drinking. The current NICE guidance is that women should be informed that getting drunk or binge drinking during pregnancy (which is defined as more than five standard drinks or seven-and-a-half UK units on a single occasion) may be harmful to the unborn baby. The Office for National Statistics (ONS) defines heavy drinking or binge drinking as more than eight units for men and more than six units for women on at least one day per week.

What do 9 units of alcohol look like?

| 1 bottle 13% wine | 1/3 bottle 40% vodka | 4 x cans 4% beer |

(Image adapted from Drinkaware information)

Most individuals considerably underestimate the amount that they are drinking and consequently their perception of how much it is safe to drink. Customs data indicate that nationally the reported alcohol consumption may represent only 55 to 60 per cent of the true figure. Data from the British Beer and Pub Association (Shen, 2012) indicate that on-trade consumption in licensed premises such as pubs, bars and restaurants has declined markedly over the last 20 years whilst domestic alcohol consumption has increased (Health and Social Information Survey, 2012, 2013). This has implications for future self-reported statistics, as alcohol consumed in the home setting is unlikely to be measured and therefore likely to be at a higher level than that consumed on a licensed premise.

The importance of measuring units is shown by the following case history.

CASE STUDY

Two sisters aged 10 and eight were diagnosed as having FAS during care proceedings. They had been taken into care for neglect at the ages of five and three. The midwife, health visitor, school and social worker had clearly recorded the neglect that the children were suffering but no one had asked about alcohol. The extended family had indicated that the mother had an alcohol problem and there were police records of her being drunk and disorderly, including during pregnancy. The health visitor had even recorded in her case notes that the mother's consumption of alcohol was "reasonable". The social worker who frequently checked the family fridge for food failed to see the significance of the large number of empty cans and bottles.

It was only when the children's birth father was being assessed as their potential carer, five years later, that he revealed the true extent of the problem. Throughout both pregnancies, his former partner was drinking up to eight cans of extra-strength lager (nine per cent) per day (36 units daily), plus three–four pints of beer (nine units) on Fridays and Saturdays (45 units per weekend day). During her second pregnancy, she was so intoxicated that she did not even realise that she was in labour. Her state of intoxication was not recorded in the prenatal notes.

USING STRUCTURED QUESTIONNAIRES

Questionnaires that can be scored and have been validated by scientific research can be very useful in identifying potential alcohol dependence. One of the problems in screening pregnant women for alcohol use is that most traditional alcohol-screening questionnaires were developed for use in men. They are much less effective in identifying drinking problems among women, particularly pregnant women. Men have different patterns of alcohol consumption and different thresholds for problem drinking. Biological differences between women and men also mean that the same quantity of alcohol consumed over the same time period produces higher blood alcohol levels in women than in men. Women are also more sensitive than men to alcohol-related organ damage.

However, researchers have now developed several simple alcohol-screening instruments for use with pregnant women, which can be administered quickly and easily, and have been evaluated and found to be effective. These are the T-ACE, the TWEAK and the Audit-C. Women alter their alcohol consumption once they learn that they are pregnant, so all three questionnaires ask about drinking patterns before pregnancy, a more accurate measure of a potential drinking problem. Women are also likely to deny or minimise their drinking during pregnancy out of embarrassment and these questionnaires have the advantage that there are no socially correct answers, particularly to the tolerance question.

The T-ACE Alcohol Screening Questionnaire

This was the first screening test to be developed for use with pregnant women. It consists of four questions and takes less than a minute to answer.

1. **T = Tolerance** How many drinks does it take to make you feel high?

2. **A = Annoyance** Have people annoyed you by criticising your drinking?

3. **C = Cut down** Have you ever felt you ought to cut down on your drinking?

4. **E = Eye-opener** Have you ever had a drink first thing in the morning to steady your nerves or to get rid of a hangover?

The test is scored as follows:

- 2 points if the answer to question 1 is two or more drinks.

- 1 point if the answer is yes to questions 2, 3 or 4.

Out of a potential total of 5 points, a score of 2 or more is suggestive of harmful drinking patterns during pregnancy.

(Source: Sokol *et al* (1989))

The TWEAK Screening Questionnaire: application process

There are two versions of the TWEAK screening questionnaire: one that is recommended for populations with high levels of binge drinking, and one that is recommended for populations with lower levels of binge drinking. (NB: these questionnaires were developed in the USA, so the drinking levels stated refer to the USA levels.)

The TWEAK questionnaire for populations with high levels of binge drinking consists of five questions:

1. **T = Tolerance** How many drinks does it take before the alcohol makes you fall asleep or pass out? Record the number of drinks (a positive score is six or more drinks).

   or

   If you never drink until you pass out, what is the largest number of drinks that you have? Record the number of drinks (a positive score is six or more drinks).

2. **W = Worried** Have your friends or relatives worried or complained about your drinking in the last year?

3. **E = Eye-opener** Do you sometimes take a drink in the morning when you first get up?

4. **A = Amnesia** Are there times when you drink and can't remember what you said or did?

5. **K = Cut down** Do you sometimes feel the need to cut down on your drinking?

The TWEAK alcohol screening questionnaire for populations with low levels of binge drinking also consists of five questions:

1. **T = Tolerance** How many drinks does it take before you begin to feel the first effects of alcohol? Record the number of drinks (a positive score is three or more drinks).

2. **W = Worried** Have your friends or relatives worried or complained about your drinking in the last year?

3. **E = Eye-opener** Do you sometimes take a drink in the morning when you first get up?

4. **A = Amnesia** Are there times when you drink and can't remember what you said or did?

5. **K = Cut down** Do you sometimes feel the need to cut down on your drinking?

For both versions, the test is scored as follows:

- A positive response to questions 1 and 2 scores two points.

- A positive response to questions 3, 4 and 5 scores one point.

Out of a total score of seven on the TWEAK test, a score of two or more points is suggestive of harmful drinking patterns during pregnancy.

(Source: Chan *et al* (1993))

The Audit-C

This is a three-question alcohol screen that can identify individuals who are hazardous drinkers. It includes the following questions:

1. How often do you have a drink containing alcohol?

   Never (0 points), monthly or less (1 point), 2–4 times per month (2 points), 2–3 times per week (3 points), 4 or more times per week (4 points)

2. How many drinks containing alcohol do you have on a typical day when you are drinking?

   0–2 (0 points), 3–4 (1 point), 5–6 (2 points), 7–9 (3 points), 10 or more (4 points)

3. How often do you have six or more drinks on one occasion?

   Never (0 points), less than monthly (1 point), monthly (2 points), weekly (3 points), daily or almost daily (4 points)

Out of a potential score of 12, it is recommended that the threshold for being a hazardous drinker should be set at more than three for women.

(Source: Frank *et al* (2008))

MANAGEMENT AND REPORTING

It is important to remember that a positive result following a screen is not an alcoholism diagnosis. It is rather an opportunity for a discussion about prenatal alcohol exposure and the risk that drinking poses to the unborn child. When these questions are routinely asked in every case, this reduces the risk of stigmatisation for the individual woman. Most pregnant women are highly motivated to change their behaviour and a short discussion may be all that is required. In other cases, further assessment or a formal referral might be necessary.

KEY LEARNING POINT

- A comprehensive range of preventive services to reduce the number of alcohol-affected pregnancies does not currently exist in the UK. The onus therefore is on individual practitioners and their partner agencies to reduce the number of damaged children in our society. A report by the All-Party Parliamentary Group for FASD, published in December 2015, concluded that alcohol has "major implications" for Government policy and recommended a massive FASD education programme right across the board. Ignorance in this field is simply not an option for anyone who works with vulnerable families and children.

Chapter 6
Diagnosis and the vital role of the social worker

I am so angry with everyone, especially the social worker and the doctor because even though I told them about my drinking, I still had to make the diagnosis myself with the help of Dr Google.

(Mother of seven-year-old boy)

There is no point in diagnosis, it's expensive and doesn't make any difference.

(Child care manager)

CONFUSING TERMINOLOGY

Early diagnosis is the key to the future successful management of the affected child. However, diagnosis is difficult and the terminology used can be confusing for professionals not involved in this field. There are several diagnostic terms used to describe alcohol-affected children, including:

- Foetal Alcohol Syndrome (FAS)
- Foetal Alcohol Effects (FAE)
- Partial Foetal Alcohol Syndrome (PFAS)
- Alcohol-Related Birth Defects (ARBD)
- Alcohol-Related Neurodevelopmental Disorder (ARND)
- Foetal Alcohol Spectrum Disorder (FASD)

This situation has arisen because our understanding of the complex impact of alcohol on the unborn child has been developing slowly over the last 50 years. Different teams of researchers have tried to separate the affected children into groups based on specific characteristics, and exposure to alcohol can have numerous adverse effects on a developing foetus, which are a spectrum of physical abnormalities, cognitive and behavioural problems.

The most damaged children with the characteristic facial features, poor growth and developmental and behavioural abnormalities are defined as having foetal alcohol syndrome (FAS). However, this diagnosis only applies to a small minority of affected children.

The umbrella term, foetal alcohol spectrum disorder (FASD), is commonly used for all the other children affected by alcohol. Although a simple and useful way of understanding the complexities of the disorder, this diagnosis can be misleading. It implies that there is a simple spectrum of severity on which any particular individual can be placed. This is simply a convenient myth. There is no such thing as a "mild foetal alcohol spectrum disorder". The effects of exposure to alcohol during development vary from individual to individual.

It is important to realise that whatever the formal diagnosis, alcohol-related disabilities vary considerably from one person to the next. Any diagnostic term must be accompanied by an insightful and individual understanding of its implications for *that particular person*. Socially, the most severely affected individuals are often those who have insufficient features to make a diagnosis but still suffer the devastating consequences of lifelong undiagnosed brain damage.

HOW FAS/FASD ARE DIAGNOSED

Diagnosis is not easy. There is no simple test, physical examination, blood test, X-ray or even MRI scan that will diagnose the condition. For many affected children, there are no obvious problems until the child is of school age. Diagnosis depends, not on a single test, but on obtaining and assessing information in four key areas. Diagnosis is not simply a medical task but one that must be shared between health and social care because a number of different professional skills are needed. The key elements are:

- a history of maternal alcohol consumption during pregnancy;
- prenatal and/or postnatal growth retardation;
- characteristic facial features;
- neurodevelopmental and behavioural characteristics.

A history of exposure to alcohol before birth

The first and most crucial element of the diagnosis is a history of exposure to alcohol before birth. Establishing the history of alcohol consumption is one of the most difficult issues in diagnosis. The pregnant woman who consumes alcohol is not always easily identified. Expectant mothers are not usually forthright about their drinking habits, nor are they necessarily able to recall the precise quantities and timing of their drinks. However, in the absence of a specific biomarker to detect alcohol exposure, this history remains pivotal in the diagnosis. Problem drinkers cannot be identified by their appearance or by socioeconomic characteristics. A documented systematic drinking history is essential and should be obtained from all birth mothers during any initial assessment.

For the looked after child, this essential information can be almost impossible to obtain. **The social worker has a vital role to play in obtaining, recording and preserving this information, which must follow the child.** There is a pivotal moment in time when this information can be collected, which is when the family is first involved with social care. Accurate information about maternal alcohol use in pregnancy, unlike drugs, is rarely systematically documented in either the child's medical or social care records. Extended family members, who are frequently being assessed as long-term carers, must be asked about a birth mother's use of alcohol. When asked, they can often give very accurate information about a woman's drinking patterns. Teachers should be asked if a mother ever collects her children from school in an intoxicated state. Police records will have evidence of drunken disorderly behaviour and domestic violence fuelled by alcohol. General practitioners will be aware of alcoholism yet may not relate this fact to child protection enquiries. Medical confidentiality still prevents access to maternal health records once the child has moved out of the birth family. "Soft information" about a family's lifestyle and functioning may not be entered on central electronic record systems. Paper records are often lost as cases are transferred between teams and adopted or fostered children leave the local area. Failure to appreciate the importance of this information makes it difficult to distinguish the effects of FASD from neglectful parenting or a host of other risk factors, often producing unjustified feelings of guilt or inadequacy in adoptive parents or foster carers. As a result, most looked after children with alcohol-induced brain damage will have the catastrophic learning and behaviour problems but will never get a formal diagnosis.

A history of poor growth before and after birth

Growth depends on a complex interplay of ethnicity, genes, parental heights, gestation, chronic ill health in childhood, nutrition and nurture. Children affected by prenatal alcohol exposure can also be unusually small in weight and/or height, both at birth and in later childhood. Adequate nutrition and a caring environment are not enough to reverse this growth failure.

Children diagnosed with FAS are usually small children who will become small adults. However, only the most severely affected children have poor growth; a significant number of children diagnosed with FASD will have normal growth patterns.

Growth can also be a difficult area to evaluate for the looked after child. There are other factors in their lives that can cause faltering growth, such as maternal cigarette smoking and drugs, poor prenatal care, neglect, poor nutrition and multiple placement moves. Early weights may have not been recorded, centile charts not filled in or the parent-held record lost. Growth deficiency caused by alcohol exposure becomes more likely when poor growth is not explained by other factors and there is no catch-up growth when the child is moved to a more nurturing environment.

Characteristic facial features

The foster carer thinks that he has FAS. We sent him to a geneticist, but the consultant couldn't be definite, so presumably he doesn't have it.

Poor geneticist, poor foster carer and poor child! No doctor can ever diagnose any condition based entirely on one physical sign. However, facial features are universally and incorrectly relied on to make a diagnosis, often in the absence of any other relevant information.

The facial features that are characteristic of FAS are shown in the lip-philtrum guide (see later in this chapter) and are:

- a short palpebral fissure (small eyes);
- a flat or smooth philtrum (the space between the upper lip and the nose that normally has a "cupid's bow" indentation is flat);
- a thin vermillion border (the red part) of the upper lip.

However, they cannot be relied on for diagnosis, for the following reasons:

- The features are caused by exposure to alcohol in the first two months of pregnancy whilst the child's face is forming. If the mother does not drink alcohol in this period, the child's face will be normal. After the face is formed, the child's features will not change. In addition, facial features only occur when there have been unusually high levels of alcohol exposure in early pregnancy. However, the brain continues to develop throughout pregnancy and is harmed by levels of exposure below that required to produce these characteristic facial features.

- The main problem with characteristic facial features as an indicator of foetal alcohol-affected individuals is poor sensitivity. There are too many false negatives; that is, affected individuals without the facial characteristics are not identified.

- Although the facial features are more apparent in late infancy and early childhood, they become less prominent as the child enters adolescence.

When diagnosing adults, it is often necessary to look at childhood photos.

- Other genetic syndromes can have similar features and must be excluded by chromosome analysis.

The majority (over 85 per cent) of children damaged by prenatal alcohol exposure have no physical birth defects. They have normal faces and normal growth but have the devastating cognitive and behavioural difficulties caused by alcohol exposure in the last three months of pregnancy. Behaviour problems are normally the main reasons for referring the child for diagnosis. These difficulties can be as severe in the child without characteristic facial features as in the child who has them. They may not be evident until early school age when the prenatal alcohol exposure is forgotten or considered irrelevant.

Neurodevelopmental and behavioural problems

Behavioural problems are normally the main reasons for referring the alcohol-affected child for diagnosis and further investigation. Affected children have a myriad of signs and symptoms: hyperactivity, impulsiveness, short memory spans, concentration difficulty, poor planning and organisational skills, poor judgement and failure to consider consequences of their actions, motor difficulties, speech and language difficulties, perceptual disorders and specific learning disabilities. This is because they have generalised organic brain damage caused by alcohol exposure that affects the executive functioning of the pre-frontal cortex of the brain. The many ways in which affected children can present are considered in detail in Chapter 8.

Lip-philtrum guides 1 (A) and 2 (B) (developed in the USA) are used to rank upper lip thinness and philtrum smoothness. The philtrum is the vertical groove between the nose and upper lip. The guides reflect the full range of lip thickness and philtrum depth with Ranks 1, 2 and 3 within the range of normal for a population and Rank 3 representing the population mean. Ranks 4 and 5 reflect the thin lip and smooth philtrum that characterize the FAS facial phenotype. Guide 1 is used for Caucasians and all other races with lips like Caucasians. Guide 2 is used for African Americans and all other races with lips as full as African Americans. Free digital images of these guides for use on smartphones and tablets can be obtained from astley@uw.edu.

FASD 4-digit Diagnostic code

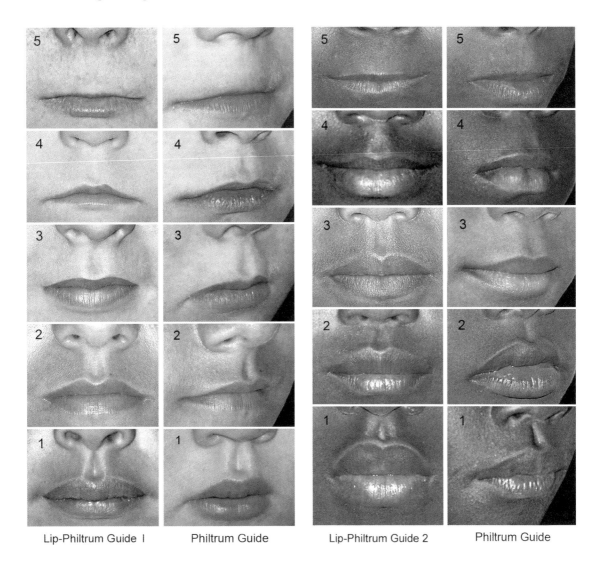

Lip-Philtrum Guide 1   Philtrum Guide   Lip-Philtrum Guide 2   Philtrum Guide

© 2017, Susan Astley PhD, University of Washington

KEY LEARNING POINT

- Diagnosis is not easy. The social worker, general practitioner, health visitor, midwife and foster carer all have a vital role to play in obtaining, recording and preserving information about a woman's lifestyle in pregnancy. This information must be recorded and preserved. The records must follow the child, especially the adopted and fostered child. Preserving this information is absolutely essential because the child may not show symptoms for many years. For more information on diagnosis, see the professional guides listed in Appendix E.

Chapter 7
Why diagnosis matters

My son went without a diagnosis for 15 years. During that time, I felt completely alone, stigmatised and isolated. When he was finally diagnosed, I wept tears of pure joy.

(Birth mother)

His behaviour was appalling, and everyone assumed that I was a terrible mother. I rarely admitted to being his biological mother and just let them assume that he was adopted.

(Mother of 10-year-old boy)

THE PRESENT UNSATISFACTORY STATE OF DIAGNOSTIC SERVICES IN THE UK

Currently, there are major difficulties in getting a diagnosis of FASD in the UK. Diagnostic services are patchy across the country. There is only one specialist national clinic (in Redhill, Surrey). There are also a small, but increasing number of paediatricians with an interest in FASD, who are developing services in their local areas. In general, however, a "postcode lottery" still operates for diagnosis. There are no gold standard, multidisciplinary assessment teams, which are now regarded as routine in the USA and Canada.

There is, as yet, no clear pathway in the UK for the referral of individuals with suspected FASD to specialist clinics to allow a complete diagnostic evaluation. There are inadequate specialist services to support and follow up these referrals. There is inconsistency as to where individuals are referred. The services to which families are referred may not necessarily have the skills required to diagnose and manage FASD effectively. The development of clear referral pathways and provision of adequate specialist services for the comprehensive diagnosis and subsequent management of FASD needs to be addressed urgently (British Medical Association, 2016).

Professional knowledge and attitudes vary. The stigma associated with diagnosis still makes some professionals reluctant to pursue the issue, especially for a child still living with their birth mother. Given this situation, is there any point in diagnosis and does it make any difference?

WHY DIAGNOSIS MATTERS

FASD is more common than most professionals appreciate, and well-intentioned practice can make a bad situation worse. Embarrassment and a reluctance to raise the issue of alcohol is counterproductive and not in either the child's, the mother's or society's best interests. Large numbers of children have been, and are being, born with this life-long untreatable condition. These children and their families suffer the consequences of both *missed diagnosis* and *mis-diagnosis*.

The missed diagnosis

For over 50 years, UK child care practice has been dominated by attachment theory and the impact of postnatal trauma, neglect and abuse. The concept of behaviour difficulties due to untreatable organic brain disease is new to most UK professionals. Unless trained in, and aware of, FASD, few professionals, including social workers, will consider pre-birth exposure to alcohol as an explanation for a child's behaviour. This lack of understanding has led to many parents and carers being unfairly blamed for their child's problems and then given the wrong strategies for managing them.

Prenatal alcohol damage can present unknowingly to a wide range of service providers. Individuals can present to the health services with physical issues, to psychiatry and psychology with behaviour problems, to education with learning problems, and in early adult life to the criminal justice system with offending behaviour. If the underlying cause of the problem is not considered at the point of referral, FASD will be missed.

These "missed diagnosed" children will instead be viewed as "poorly behaved", "non-compliant" or "conduct disordered" children. Their parents risk being criticised for being poor carers. However, the children and their families continue to experience problems that get worse as the child gets older. The family receives little support, and parents feel increasingly isolated and guilty. In severe cases, the situation may lead to family breakdown. The children then end up in care, are difficult to place, and suffer the additional trauma of multiple placements or residential behavioural units.

The mis-diagnosis

These are alcohol-exposed children who are given multiple, different and inaccurate diagnoses. They are diagnosed with ADHD, atypical autism, an attachment disorder or a conduct disorder. They risk being treated inappropriately with medication or having expensive "talking therapies" that are unlikely to work. The children are often taken from professional to professional, accumulating diagnoses as they grow older. Families and social workers are on a "diagnostic merry-go-round" in the vain hope that a new diagnosis will explain the child's difficulties and provide a "cure" for their problems. Resources are wasted on numerous assessments, repeated visits, unnecessary appointments and inappropriate treatment. Families are progressively driven to despair.

Diagnosis affects prognosis

Without a diagnosis, appropriate intervention and family support, the outcomes for affected individuals can be very negative. For example, a long-term USA cohort study that followed up a group of affected individuals for over 30 years identified that, by the time they were adults, 90 per cent had mental health problems, 50 per cent were in prison, 30 per cent had their own drug and alcohol problems, with a further 50 per cent having problems with inappropriate sexualised behaviour. Girls were vulnerable to exploitation and rape with boys sometimes being perpetrators of harm (Streissguth and O'Malley, 2000).

Diagnosis improves the prognosis. Where good outcomes were seen, early intervention had usually been provided. Streissguth and O'Malley (2000) identified the following protective factors:

- Living in a stable and nurturing home environment for over 72 per cent of life. Stability between the ages of 8 and 12 appeared to be particularly critical.

- Being accurately diagnosed with FAS before the age of six.

- Receiving appropriate early education.

- Being eligible for special needs services.

- Never having experienced violence or abuse.

  The prognosis was inversely related to the number of moves made by the child. The more placement moves a child had made, the worse the long-term outcome.

Failure to diagnose is not in either the mother's or society's best interests

It is often forgotten that there are also considerable risks for the birth mother in not making a diagnosis. An FASD diagnosis in her child compels the birth mother to confront her alcohol dependence, and the birth of a damaged child is often the point at which she finally addresses her drinking. However, she cannot be offered help if her alcohol dependence is ignored by professionals. She will remain in denial and continue to drink.

For the birth mother whose child is removed, the risk is that she will misuse more alcohol to cope with her emotional pain and distress. Her dependence on alcohol will get worse. Any children still left at home with her will suffer from increasing levels of neglect. The birth mother may also become pregnant again and the damage to her developing foetus increases as she gets older and her drinking escalates. Her next child will be even more severely affected than the one just removed. The risk of FASD in a pregnancy after the birth of an affected child is 77 per cent (771 per 1,000) compared to the general population risk of one per cent. Social and health costs will multiply and the downward spiral will continue.

No diagnosis now means no services in the future

Finally, without a willingness to make more diagnoses, backed up by a proper prevalence study in the UK population, there will continue to be confusion around numbers of affected individuals in our society and it will be impossible to persuade health and social service commissioners of the need for additional services. They will continue to wrongly assume that FASD is a rare disorder that they do not need to resource.

WHY DIAGNOSIS REALLY MATTERS FOR LOOKED AFTER CHILDREN

Recent research suggests that the number of affected children jumps alarmingly when the likelihood of children in care being affected is considered in more depth. Only two UK studies have been undertaken (Selwyn and Wijedesa, 2011; Gregory et al, 2015). Selwyn and Wijedasa analysed the case files of 120 black and minority ethnic children from three local authorities who had received an adoption recommendation. In approximately one-third of the cases, parental drug or alcohol misuse led to the children becoming looked after. Dr Geraldine Gregory's local audit in Peterborough found that 34 per cent of children referred to her for looked after health assessments and 75 per cent of children referred for adoption medicals had a history of prenatal alcohol exposure. In most cases, the information on prenatal alcohol and/or drug exposure came to light only during her medical assessment. In only a very few cases was the information provided as part of the social care request for assessment.

If FASD is not considered as a possibility, and because the neurological impact of alcohol does not usually present until the child is aged at least five years or even older, social workers will be unknowingly placing children for permanence with unprepared or even elderly carers. Placements will break down because of the challenges the child presents, the incorrect advice given to carers about managing the child and the absence of effective support. This issue is becoming even more urgent as the number of special guardianship orders and kinship placements steadily increases. Children are now being placed more frequently with carers who are likely to be older and less active and who may be unable to manage the child long term.

Due to inadequate information about their exposure to alcohol, children will continue to be placed with adopters, long-term foster or kinship carers who have no prior knowledge of possible long-term problems and who have had no training in the management of the alcohol-affected child. These families face years of unresolved anxiety, guilt and unanswered questions. For all parents and carers, there is a major emotional impact in being given a diagnosis many years after placement. For some, it will be a relief to know at last "what is wrong". Others will be angry that they were kept in the dark and given inadequate explanations that did not address their concerns. All families must come to terms with the fact that they have a child who is likely to have continuing long-term special needs and who will have an impact on the whole family.

Alcohol-dependent mothers frequently have several children in quick succession. Over time, her dependence on alcohol gets worse and the amount of alcohol she drinks in pregnancy increases. Her children become progressively more damaged, with the youngest being the most severely affected. To keep siblings together, the same adoptive family might be asked to take a number of these children, either all together or over a period of several years. FASD charities report that some adopters are caring for three, four or five siblings, all of whom have been exposed to alcohol before birth. Each child may have few problems initially, but their needs become more complex and challenging as they get older. There is a limit to how many children and how many problems a family can manage. Every family has its breaking point, as this case history shows.

CASE STUDY

A professional couple had three attractive, healthy sisters placed with them for adoption. The children had relatively few problems initially. The oldest child developed behaviour problems in secondary school and for many years refused to attend. She is now 16 and out of education.

The middle child developed problems in primary school and is currently in a small specialised behaviour unit. The youngest child was unable to go to nursery because of her aggressive outbursts and the education authority is looking for a primary school that will take her. The parents felt angry and isolated and that they were being held responsible for the way their children behaved.

It was only when the youngest child was diagnosed with FAS that the family's problems began to make sense. They eventually found out that the children's birth mother had consumed substantial amounts of vodka during pregnancy, in addition to her known cocaine habit. All three children were damaged by this prenatal alcohol. Typically, the oldest child was the least damaged, the youngest the most severely affected. This well-known pattern reflects their birth mother's increased drinking as she got older and became more alcohol dependent. Brain damage meant that all the children simply could not cope with the demands of school. The adoptive parents are now in their late 50s. It seems likely that none of their children will ever be independent. The adoptive mother has had to give up her job and with it her pension. She has been driven to the point of breakdown on several occasions. Despite the provisions of the Children Act 1989 for "children in need", the family has been assessed as ineligible for respite care or an adoption allowance. They are very fearful of the future but remain totally committed to the children.

Sadly, most affected individuals get their main support from FASD charitable organisations, or local family support groups run by parents with an affected child, or the American and Canadian websites. Unless there is a radical shift in professional knowledge and practice, diagnosis and support will continue to be undertaken not by multi-disciplinary professional teams but by desperate carers helped only by "Dr Google".

KEY LEARNING POINT

- Given the high numbers of affected children in the care system and the implications for permanent placement, it is vital that social workers become familiar with FASD and always question, at the earliest possible opportunity, whether pre-birth alcohol consumption might play a part in the child's difficulties.

Chapter 8

How presentation varies with age

My child is in permanent conflict with a world she doesn't understand and cannot make sense of.

(Birth mother)

We cannot predict the degree of damage or the eventual outcome. We can only manage our expectations. That's one of the secrets to staying sane.

(Adoptive parents)

Superficially my daughter appears to be so capable but actually has no ability to cope with school at any level.

(Adoptive parent)

The main burden of caring for children affected by alcohol is caused by their long-term problems with learning, language and behaviour. The pattern of these difficulties changes as the child moves from infancy to adulthood and the impact of the damage presents in different ways at different ages. Individually, the affected children can show very different patterns of strengths and difficulties because of the unpredictable nature of the pre-birth damage to the frontal lobes of the brain.

INFANTS AND TODDLERS

At this age, the symptoms are vague, non-specific and not diagnostic. Infants are often tremulous and irritable or may spend prolonged periods of time sleeping. They have a weak sucking reflex and may have feeding difficulties. They are often uninterested in food and feeding can take hours. Eating difficulties are a major source of stress for parents. Some children overeat, some undereat, some eat very slowly, while others never seem to feel hungry. Despite adequate nutrition, an affected child may gain weight only very slowly. Children are frequently referred to hospital for investigation of their poor weight gain or failure to thrive.

Sleep, or the lack of it, is a big issue, particularly in very young children. Patterns vary – an affected child either needs more sleep than other children or does not sleep at all. Sleep problems have a number of different causes. Affected children often lack an internal body clock and have no concept of time. They struggle to differentiate between night and day and to understand that night time means sleep. They have erratic sleep patterns with no predictable sleep–wake cycle. For all carers, it is exhausting and challenging to care for a child who does not sleep, engaging in a nightly battle to establish a regular sleeping routine.

As toddlers, the lack of interest in food, slow weight gain and disrupted sleep pattern continues. Affected children have a low muscle tone and can be slow to achieve their developmental milestones. They struggle with fine motor skills, holding a pencil, learning to dress and undress, and using a spoon and fork. They can be hypersensitive to noise, bright lights, temperature and touch. Toilet training can be slow.

Speech often develops very early and the children can be excessively talkative. They are very sociable but over-friendly and indiscriminate with relationships. They have a short attention span and are easily distracted and hyperactive. They tend to move from one activity to another, showing little in the way of focused play. They are unable to comprehend danger and do not respond well to repeated verbal warnings. They are prone to temper tantrums and non-compliance. They respond badly to change and prefer routine.

The child's carers are left with a growing feeling that "something is not quite right" but cannot identify what is wrong. They are given a lot of well-meaning, often contradictory advice from family, friends and even child care professionals but nothing really seems to work. The gap between the behaviour of an alcohol-affected child and their peers steadily widens as the child gets older.

SCHOOL-AGED CHILDREN

During the early years in school, the typical child begins to develop better concentration, more social interaction and an increasing capacity to learn new skills, particularly literacy and numeracy. For the child with FASD, it is often in school that their problems first become more noticeable as the child begins to show difficulties across multiple areas.

Children affected by prenatal alcohol have deficits in the executive function of the brain. This is essential for:

- organisation and planning;

- focusing and maintaining attention;

- storing and retrieving memories;

- inhibiting inappropriate actions;

- stopping emotions from getting out of control;

- understanding social situations and social behaviour;

- abstract thinking.

   The affected child will therefore show some, or even all, of the following difficulties.

- Attention deficits and poor impulse control become more apparent as the demands for classroom attention increase. An affected child will find it difficult to wait for their turn, to follow rules or to co-operate. They often interrupt the work or play of others and are inappropriately intrusive. Consequently, FASD is often incorrectly diagnosed as attention deficit hyperactivity disorder (ADHD) and treated inappropriately with medication that is ineffective or that may even make the child worse.

- The child's memory, especially memory for language, is weak. The child needs constant repetition and reminders for even basic activities at home and school. Information is learned, retained for a while and then lost. The child may tell you that they understand your instructions, but then is unable to carry them out. Children rapidly learn to act as though they understand, but cannot follow a series of actions through by themselves. They often watch and follow another child who knows what to do. Language-based behavioural strategies or talking therapies are usually ineffective.

- The child exists in the "here and now". They are unable to monitor their own work or behaviour, cannot transfer learning from one situation to another or learn from experience. Their behaviour patterns can be inflexible. Their logic is faulty and they lack critical thinking and judgement skills. They have difficulty in abandoning strategies that have proved to be ineffective in the past and are unable to apply previously learnt rules to a new situation.

- Affected children often have good verbal skills, a superficially friendly social manner and obvious good intentions that mask the seriousness of their problems. They talk too much and too quickly but have little real information to communicate. They like to be the centre of attention and their outgoing and friendly manner, which is often seen as positive in early childhood, becomes more problematic as the child grows older. They are increasingly seen as immature and naïve. They have poor peer relations and can become progressively socially isolated, preferring to play with younger children or adults rather than with their peer group. Consequently, FASD is often incorrectly diagnosed as an autistic spectrum disorder.

- As they progress through school, the affected child's reading and spelling skills usually peak. They have increasing difficulty in completing assignments and mastering new academic subjects. As they are usually very concrete thinkers, they have trouble working with ideas. They have increasing problems with abstract thinking and are unable to link cause and effect. They struggle to understand concepts, especially mathematical ideas, money and time. They find it difficult to identify and label emotions or feelings. They tend to fall further behind their peers as schoolwork becomes increasingly abstract and concept-based.

- Affected children are frequently misjudged as being lazy, stubborn and unwilling to learn. Their skills in school can often fluctuate from day to day, giving the mistaken impression that their poor performance is deliberate.

- During the first two years in primary school, most affected children will achieve some basic reading and writing skills and the extent of any learning delay may not be initially apparent. In a good primary school where there is a lot of structure and routine, some children will not present until this structure is taken away, normally in a secondary school setting. Sadly, very many affected children will fail in school because in addition to a low normal IQ, they lack the core abilities needed to learn and succeed: sitting still, listening, concentrating, understanding cause and effect, following complex verbal instructions, planning, and organising their time.

ADOLESCENCE AND ADULTHOOD

As an affected child matures into adolescence and adulthood, any facial deformities become less noticeable but the short stature and microcephaly (small head) remain. Unfortunately, by this stage, the child will have often been affected by other factors that complicate the presentation. Trauma, bullying, abuse, educational failure and placement moves can become routine. For the looked after child, the documentation of these events may be missing or unavailable. Puberty complicates the presentation even further. A combination of poor understanding, communication problems, an inability to always recall what was said plus their struggles to cope with everyday life can lead to secondary problems with depression, anxiety and low self-esteem that further affect the young person's functioning.

Where children are diagnosed early and followed up, many of these issues can be minimised. Without diagnosis, adults affected by prenatal alcohol experience major psychosocial and adjustment problems for the rest of their lives. They have difficulty holding down jobs, problems managing money, poor social skills, low motivation and may become increasingly withdrawn and isolated. Antisocial behaviour and inability to live independently are common. Affected adults are more likely to have problems with alcoholism or drug abuse themselves. They have difficulty showing remorse or taking responsibility for their actions, and frequently behave in ways that place themselves or others at risk. A high degree of impulsivity and a total lack of inhibition mean that affected individuals are easily influenced and subject to peer manipulation and exploitation. They are at high risk for sexual abuse, problems with the police and involvement in the criminal justice system.

STRENGTHS OF THE FASD CHILD

Although the difficulties that alcohol-affected children experience are lifelong and the underlying brain damage is untreatable, FASD is not a hopeless diagnosis. As individuals, these children have a complex profile with a mixed pattern of major weaknesses and real strengths. It is essential to recognise and reinforce these strengths, which will increase the child's confidence and self-esteem. They can also be used as strategies for education and behaviour management.

Parents usually describe their affected children with great affection as loving, caring, kind, sensitive, loyal and compassionate. They are often friendly, cheerful and outgoing individuals who can flourish in an accepting or modified environment. They can be energetic, determined and very hardworking if they have the right skills to complete a task. They have a very strong sense of fair play and are co-operative and loyal. They are curious and like to be involved in family and social activities. They are empathetic to very young children, the elderly and animals, with whom they are nurturing, sensitive and gentle. They often have exceptionally good, long-term visual memories and can be wonderful storytellers with a rich fantasy life. They can be curious and questioning with a profound sense of wonder. Many have artistic, musical or creative skills and enjoy tasks such as cooking or gardening.

KEY LEARNING POINT

- FASD is not a hopeless diagnosis. Consistent, patient, loving, "industrial-strength" parenting with structure and appropriate expectations plus support in school can help affected children to reach their full potential. That potential will be limited by alcohol-related brain damage but setting the bar at the right height, and identifying what a child can do versus what they cannot do, will help them achieve some success in their life. Above all, early diagnosis will hopefully prevent some of the "secondary disabilities" that blight the lives of these children and their families.

Chapter 9
What does not work and why

What is the point of telling us what does not work, I only want to know what does.

(Social worker)

For a long time, we parented this child the same way that we parented our children who don't have brain damage. We wound up frustrated and hopeless and our children ended up confused and angry.

(Adoptive parent)

Before discussing those strategies and parenting methods that are likely to work, it is important to mention those that do not help the alcohol-affected child. Alcohol-affected children do not respond like typically developing children. Behaviour due to organic brain damage can be changed, but cannot be changed easily. Although children with FASD can be as naughty as any other children, the majority of their undesirable behaviours are due to their faulty memory, social ineptness, lack of impulse control or being completely overwhelmed by the environment around them. Giving advice to a parent that does not work increases both the parent's and child's sense of failure. The family will also lose their confidence and trust in the professional who gave it. "First do no harm" is always an important ethical principle when working with vulnerable families.

The following approaches will usually be unsuccessful or even make the situation worse.

TRADITIONAL PARENTING TECHNIQUES

Parenting classes are big business. A recent Google search produced over two million sites advertising positive parenting. Unfortunately, the most unsuccessful strategies with alcohol-affected children are these traditional parenting techniques. Traditional behaviour management consists essentially of rewarding "good" behaviour and ignoring the "bad" to effect change in a child's behaviour. This strategy is universally taught on most parenting courses and is found in most parenting manuals. Nearly all the parents with an affected child will have been advised to try these techniques, and will have failed.

For these techniques to work, the child must understand cause and effect, must have some understanding of the impact of their behaviour on others and must have some concept of "future earning", i.e. the child must understand that behaving in the right way now will bring a reward in the future. The alcohol-affected child does not have any of these skills. They live in the "here and now" and have a high level of impulsivity. They frequently fail to use their previous experience to work out the consequences of their present actions. Their difficulty with abstract and flexible thinking means that they also struggle to imagine what might go wrong – so they repeat the same mistakes over and over again.

Stickers, tokens and star charts

Stickers, tokens and star charts do not work with alcohol-affected children. This is because affected children do not learn from their mistakes. They live in the moment and accept life as it happens. The child may not link the reward to the behaviour, whether good or bad. They may not even understand the words "good" or "bad" when used in the concept of behaviour. They have a poor memory and no concept of time. The sticker given as a reward on Monday is forgotten by Monday night, and almost certainly has no impact by Tuesday. For the same reasons, cancelling future trips or treats is unlikely to be successful.

Time out, the naughty step, thinking time, being sent to your room

Problems with sensory overload frequently lead to emotional outbursts that the affected child does not know how to stop. The brain of the child with FASD is like a simmering pot and even the slightest frustration can cause him or her to boil over emotionally. A naughty step or chair will not help the child to self-regulate and calm down. Time out is unlikely to prevent a behaviour recurring, will not produce any useful learning, and could make behaviour worse. Deficits in the executive function of the brain also mean that the child may have no understanding of the link between the outburst and the time out. In addition, the alcohol-affected child has a very impaired concept of time and literally has no idea if the time out period is long or short.

It is better instead to find a place for the child that is comfortable and quiet. This might be the child's bedroom or a room away from other household activities. The most important thing is to significantly reduce the stress the child is feeling from noise and chaos. This "comfort corner", which is not a punishment zone, might have a squashy bean bag, a soft quilt, subdued lighting and headphones playing favourite soothing music. Removing the child from the situation and giving them a tool for controlling outbursts in the future is more likely to be successful than time out. The child will usually tell his or her parents when he or she is feeling calm enough to return to family life.

Using money as a reward

Using money as a reward will also be unsuccessful. Money is a very abstract concept. You can touch money and hold it in your hand, but what money can buy or what money can do are abstract ideas. For this strategy to work, the child needs to have a concept of the value of money, understand that an amount of money will only last a certain amount of time depending on how much you spend, and realise that impulsive spending uses all your money in one go. Most individuals with FASD will need help in managing money all their lives.

Using abstract language and complicated instructions

Often the so-called "naughty" behaviour of the child is due to an inability to control their impulses. They see something, they like it, they touch it and take it. They have no concept of ownership or property – two more very abstract concepts. No one is holding the object they want, it is just sitting on a shelf in a shop or supermarket, so how can it "belong" to someone else? They are then further confused when an adult uses abstract language in a complex sentence, such as: 'You should not take something that belongs to someone else', or 'How many times have I told you not to do that?', or 'Why did you do that?'. These expressions are unlikely to get any response from a child whose understanding of language is significantly delayed.

TALKING THERAPIES

Another solution frequently offered to the affected child and family are so-called "talking therapies". These do not work with the alcohol-affected child. The children have a poor understanding of complex verbal language, particularly abstract language that involves talking about feelings. They have impaired memories. They are unable to sequence events and unable to understand time. When the therapist talks about a behaviour that has occurred in the past, the child can think that this is the behaviour that they should be displaying now. The wrong therapeutic approach, combined with the child's difficulty in grasping concepts and understanding emotions, only adds to their confusion and unhappiness. Similarly, life story work with adopted and fostered children is often of limited value because of the child's difficulty with memory and understanding timeframes.

BEING PUNITIVE AND MOVING THE CHILD

It should not really be necessary to add being punitive to this list. Being punitive will always fail. Sadly, society can be punitive to the carers of children with FASD because the behaviour of the child is so bizarre and difficult to understand. The bizarre behaviour is often mistakenly blamed on the child's parents or the home environment. In a misguided attempt to help the family, the parents can be asked by well-meaning professionals to undertake a traditional parenting course. When the parents attempt to follow the techniques they have been taught, implementation is at best a complete failure, and at worst, makes the family situation worse. The parents are then blamed for not implementing the techniques properly, rather than the techniques themselves being recognised as wrong and unhelpful in this situation. Afterwards, the parents are understandably reluctant to be honest about how little the family situation has changed. They keep the seriousness of their concerns to themselves, are more reluctant to ask for help in the future, and the family's problems spiral downwards.

Foster carers have even been threatened with the removal of a child and some have actually had a child removed from a placement because they were unfairly judged as not successfully managing the child. A child exposed to alcohol before birth has organic brain damage. Removing a child to a new set of carers will not cure this. Subjecting the family to child protection procedures will also fail. Even therapeutic foster care will not work unless the carers have been very specifically trained.

KEY LEARNING POINT

- Do not give parents a map of Birmingham and then tell them to find their way around London. Do not be surprised when they fail!

Chapter 10
Incorrect assumptions and what is really happening

Children damaged by prenatal alcohol can present with a myriad of signs, symptoms and challenging behaviours. The temptation for parents and professionals is to ascribe each new issue to a separate cause. Over time, this can mean that the child has numerous professional assessments and the parents are progressively given multiple explanations and new diagnoses. It is not unusual to find an alcohol-affected child diagnosed as having ADHD, an autism spectrum disorder, an attachment disorder, post-traumatic stress disorder, conduct disorder and a learning disability. Families become increasingly confused by these multiple diagnoses, none of which explain the totality of the child's problems.

The common presenting behaviours listed in the table below can all be explained by damage to the prefrontal cortex of the brain leading to deficits in executive functioning. The alcohol-affected child needs only one overarching diagnosis and this table provides an explanation for a number of common behaviours and traits.

BEHAVIOUR	WHAT WE THINK	THE REAL PROBLEM
• Making the same mistakes repeatedly • Does not get the obvious	• Doing it on purpose • Manipulative • Attention seeking	• Cannot translate verbal instructions into action • Does not learn from experience and needs constant repetition to learn • Poor memory
• Will not do it • Not obeying instructions	• Doing it on purpose • Attention seeking • Stubborn • Conduct disorder	• Cannot do it • Does not understand verbal instructions • Needs time to process verbal information

BEHAVIOUR	WHAT WE THINK	THE REAL PROBLEM
• Lazy • Does not try • Late for everything	• Doing it on purpose • Attention seeking • Poor parenting	• Exhausted with trying • Fluctuating day-to-day performance recognised part of syndrome • Has no concept of time
• Over-friendly • No boundaries • Poor social judgement • Easily manipulated by others • Does not care about feelings	• Doing it on purpose • Naïve • Abused child • Trauma • Has autistic spectrum disorder	• Developmental and social age is half chronological age • Does not understand social behaviour of others • Confused in new social environment and does not know how to behave • Does not understand feelings and needs to be taught about them
• Disorganised, untidy • Refuses to sit still • Fussy and demanding	• Doing it on purpose • Attention seeking • Manipulative • Wants to bother others • Poor parenting • Has ADHD – needs medication	• Hyper- or hypo-sensitivity to touch and other sensations • Unable to cope in very stimulating social environments
• Steals and tells lies	• Doing it on purpose • Attention seeking • Has a conduct disorder • Poor parenting, dysfunctional family • Abuse	• Poor memory – fills in "gaps" with other remembered incidents or things seen on TV • Does not understand the abstract concept of ownership

BEHAVIOUR	WHAT WE THINK	THE REAL PROBLEM
• Behaves like a child • Always in trouble at home and school • Truancy • Gets lost • Loses things • Temper tantrums	• Doing it on purpose • Attention seeking • Has a conduct disorder • Has a learning disability • Poor parenting • Wrong foster home • Abuse	• Is a child • Developmental and social age is half chronological age • Deficits masked by good verbal skills • Unable to process information and cannot cope with increasing demands of school, uses "meltdowns" to escape • Poor memory • Overwhelmed by noise, lights, sounds and cognitive demands • Increasing awareness of own disability

Adapted for a UK audience from *Strategies not Solutions*, first published by the Edmonton and Area Fetal Alcohol Network, Alberta, Canada

© This amended version Mary Mather 2017

Chapter 11

What does work

What we need as a family is to be surrounded by people who really understand our daughter. We only found this in our local church. In this community, my child has friends and even the beginnings of independence. We can relax knowing that whatever she does people understand and protect her.

(Adoptive parent)

The hairdressers is one of the very few places I can go to relax because they actually let a 12-year-old boy play in their staff room, happily sorting out curlers whilst I have my hair done.

(Adoptive parent)

If we cannot manage the brain damage caused by prenatal alcohol exposure, we can just manage our expectations and stay sane!

(Grandmother bringing up her three affected grandchildren)

There are a number of key guidelines in managing the child with FASD. However, it is important to remember that all children, alcohol-affected or not, are first and foremost individuals with distinct personalities, preferences and temperaments. Parenting tips that may work wonders with one child may prove inappropriate and ineffective for another. The following general strategies will usually help all alcohol-affected children. Strategies for more specific behavioural problems and guides for parents are referenced in the parenting guides in Appendix B.

OWNING THE DIAGNOSIS, OR COMING TO TERMS WITH REALITY

A child disabled by alcohol exposure arouses strong emotions. Birth mothers will feel very guilty, whilst members of her extended family often feel very angry. Adopters, foster carers and kinship carers can feel a sense of failure or they may be angry that they have been misled about the severity of the child's problem. Everyone must come to terms with their senses of loss and the realisation of what might have been. However, after the initial stages of grief and anger, most parents, carers and even professionals will develop a strong desire to "fix" the problem and make everything all right. This understandable desire to fix things can get in the way of helping the child, leading to multiple consultations, referrals, wrong diagnoses and inappropriate treatment.

Everyone, including the child, must accept that there is no cure. This is a lifelong condition and one that must be managed and not solved. Whilst every effort should be made to enable the child to reach his or her full potential, this must be tempered with an acceptance that any potential may be very limited. We need strategies, not solutions, where creative support enables the affected child to become a contributing member of society. Parents and carers who realise that their child's misbehavior is due to their underlying disability, rather than willful disobedience, are more likely to be successful.

EARLY DIAGNOSIS

Professor Ann Streissguth, who is based at the University of Washington, Seattle, USA, has carried out detailed research over 40 years following the developmental outcomes for a large group of people affected by prenatal alcohol. One of her earliest findings was that those children who do best have a clear diagnosis. Being diagnosed before the age of six was associated with the best outcomes. Therefore, anything that can be done to achieve a diagnosis for an affected child will have a positive effect on their future life.

ROUTINES, ROUTINES AND MORE ROUTINES, STRUCTURE AND CONSISTENCY

The child with FASD thinks very differently from other children. Working memory problems mean that the child finds it difficult to "hold information". A major difference is their inability to learn new behaviours and they need constant repetition to learn new things. One of the most important things parents and carers can do for their child is to be very consistent in their daily routine. They need to develop a schedule and stick to it, day in and day out, schooldays and weekends. Changes in routine, especially highly-charged social activities such as birthday parties, weddings and Christmas may simply be too overwhelming for a child with FASD. Behaviour frequently deteriorates in school at times of educational transition such as a new teacher, a new classroom or moving to a new school. Placement moves that change everything in the child's life are especially destabilising. Another of Professor Streissguth's findings was that the children with FASD who do very badly are those who had a number of placement moves – the more moves the child had, the worse their long-term prognosis. When change is going to occur, this must always be explained to the child in advance and they must be prepared for it. Consistency and routine will minimise the negative impact of the change and if a child has to move to a new foster home, carers should try to keep the daily routines as fixed as possible.

CHANGE THE ENVIRONMENT, NOT THE CHILD

The brain of the alcohol-damaged child is disorganised and the way in which the various parts of the brain connect with and "talk" to each other is slower than in unaffected children. This affects the child's thinking speeds and problem-solving ability. The brain of an affected child needs to work much harder than the brain of an unaffected child in just about everything. This causes them to be easily tired and over-stimulated. Using pre-emptive strategies to try to change the environment in a way that better fits the child's needs will decrease the child's confusion and reduce the number of behavioural outbursts. These simple strategies will also increase the confidence of the caregivers and decrease their level of frustration with the child!

Daily activities need to be broken down into specific steps. Parents and carers should try to do everything in the same way and in the same order every day, for example, waking the child in the same predictable way each morning and having a predictable bedtime routine. Do not change the routine on holiday or weekend visits to family and friends. Placing labels on the outside of drawers, cupboards and using single words or pictures to indicate the contents will help the child to become more independent in dressing and undressing.

Use visual timetables or planners to help the child feel less anxious about what is going to happen next. Use photos of actual people, places, and important things to prepare a child for events such as moving to a new home, going to the dentist or doctor, going to the hospital, going to a new school, and family holidays. The unexpected or unexplained absence of a family member, even for a short holiday, can be very upsetting to the child. Use photos of the person and the place where they are to explain their absence.

If the child is hypersensitive to touch, avoid itchy, rough clothing. Use soft, loose, more easily tolerated material. Remove tags from clothing, wash new clothes before wearing and turn socks with seams inside out. If the child has difficulty understanding boundaries and private spaces, such as shared bedrooms, marking off areas with masking tape may be helpful.

Store things together by a system (e.g. by type, size, colour, etc). Have a place for everything and make sure that everything is put back in its place. Allow only one item, especially distracting items, like brightly coloured or musical toys, out at a time.

AVOID LONG, COMPLICATED EXPLANATIONS AND INSTRUCTIONS

Most parents, carers and teachers assume that a child's understanding and spoken language are at the same level of development. This pattern does not occur in the alcohol-affected child. It is quite common to have a five-year-old child with FASD whose expressive language is at the level of a seven-year-old, but whose receptive understanding of language is that of a two-year-old. A superficially articulate, streetwise teenager may only understand language that is at the level of a six-year-old. Unless this gap between understanding and spoken language is specifically assessed, it is usually missed. However, it has major consequences for the child and his or her family. Although they can appear outwardly articulate, affected children struggle to understand what is said to them. They cannot process subtle and abstract language, understand sarcasm or irony and struggle with the subtle nuances that make up our social world.

Lecturing does not work for any children, but for children with FASD it is downright perplexing. When a child genuinely does not understand what they are being asked to do, they simply cannot do it! This apparent refusal to obey instructions is not the behaviour of a child who *won't*, but of a child who *can't* do what is being asked of them. Unless the problem with understanding verbal instructions is recognised, there is a real risk that the child will become labelled as naughty, disobedient or even oppositional and defiant. The child is then shouted at, told off, punished or given consequences for their failure to obey. However, punishment only increases the child's sense of failure and makes them even more insecure and frightened.

When a child needs to understand an instruction, the language used must be as brief and simple as possible. Begin all conversations with the child's name and make eye contact with them. Use their name and ensure that you have their full attention before you speak. The child may have a short attention span, even though they may appear to be listening. In school, expressions that start with "class" or "group" or "children" will be ignored. Teachers should not be surprised when the child does not respond to greetings such as 'Good morning, class', or 'The red table can go out to play now'.

One-step, not two- or three-step, instructions are essential because the affected child has problems with working memory. Adults need to be very clear, very concrete, very direct and say exactly what they want the child to do. For example, 'Tidy up this room' is far too abstract. It is better to say, 'Pick up the bricks and put them in this box'. After praising the completed task, it can then be followed by another simple instruction, such as, 'Now put all the pencils in this tin'. Saying, 'Sit on that chair and play with your Lego' is better than shouting, 'Stop messing about'. 'Put your coat on the hook on the door' is far better than 'How many times have I told you not to leave your coat on the floor?'

The same simple, direct phrases need to be used for daily routines. 'Brush your teeth' is much better than 'Clean your teeth', or even worse, 'Time to do your teeth'. 'Put your school coat on' is better than 'We are going to be late for school again if you don't hurry'. A series of sequential pictures pinned to the wall that can be ticked off when the action is completed may help with the understanding of a complex routine such as getting ready for bed and help the child to become more independent.

The affected child will find all negative instructions confusing. He or she needs to be told what the parent or carer wants them to do, not what they *don't* want them to do. For example, instead of shouting, 'Don't run', it is better to say instead, 'Walk, please'. Two- and three-step directions should be introduced very gradually and only when the parent or carer is sure that their child can consistently follow all one-step directions.

Even when the child understands what is being asked of them, he or she will take longer to process the answer to a question. This is because to formulate a reply, the child will need to retrieve information from their memory. For example, 'What did you do at school today?' is a deceptively simple question but one that needs a memory of what has happened in the last six hours.

Finally, the child has to plan and organise themselves to comply with an instruction. Affected children struggle with sequencing, remembering instructions and are very easily distracted. For example, a parent may say, 'Go upstairs and put these clean clothes on your bed'. The child will go upstairs but, much to the parent's frustration, will be found half an hour later still in their bedroom with the clothes on the floor, doing something completely different.

Affected children are also often accused of telling lies. The individuals who do this are often less severely affected and consequently more defensive and aware of their deficits. Their faulty memories and inability to sequence events in time means that they tend to "fill in the gaps" to answer a question. Some children become quite adept at using this coping strategy and can tell very credible stories to compensate for their lack of understanding. They will frequently respond by talking about an incident they have seen on the TV or use another memory of something that happened to them in the past. Unfortunately, this means that the child now adds untruthfulness to their increasing list of undesirable behaviours.

MANAGE AND WHERE POSSIBLE AVOID MELTDOWNS

One of the main reasons for meltdowns, tantrums and outbursts of aggressive behaviour in affected children is overstimulation. Children with FASD are over-sensitive and easily overwhelmed by their environment. The affected child may find it very difficult to screen out background noise. They become distressed, throw a tantrum and then "get stuck". They are unable to stop the tantrum because they do not know what to do next and are poor at self-soothing. They do not cope well with transitions and find it very difficult to end one activity and start another. They can get stuck in one activity and are unable or unwilling to move on. Asking them to stop what they are doing often causes a tantrum.

Prevention is always the key. Frequently, it is environmental factors and external things in the world around the child that trigger the meltdown. It helps to avoid situations where the child is over-stimulated by light, movement, sound, toys, noise, colour, activities or crowds. One of the reasons parenting these children is such hard work is the pre-planning and analysis that their parents or carers have to do. They need to take time to step back, consider, reflect, think through and identify what "triggers" their child's behaviour.

It is helpful for parents to designate a calm, cosy, comfortable place for "quiet time and space" where the child can go when they feel they are becoming overwhelmed. This strategy will, over time, help the child to learn to self-regulate their out-of-control emotions. It should be made very clear that this "quiet time" is not a punishment and the "quiet space" is not a "naughty corner". An older child might like to be in their bedroom with the curtains closed or the lights dimmed, with relaxing music playing. Younger children often prefer a pile of cushions or blankets in a room where they are close to their parents or carers. Some parents and carers find a "tent" made by putting a blanket over a table or settee helpful. If anger is a problem, have a safe place for the child to express it in some physical manner, for example, bouncing on a trampoline, kicking a ball or hitting a beanbag.

Whilst prevention is always the best choice, there will still be times when an eruption occurs. Hard though it is, parents and carers must be patient, or the situation will escalate out of control as they become more stressed. No matter how frustrated and angry they are, shouting, losing one's temper, arguing with a child or physically punishing them will always make the situation worse. Children need help with a situation they find bewildering. Adults losing control and becoming angry with them will always add to their fear and distress and their feeling that the situation is now totally beyond anyone's control. Parents need a clear, predictable, individual routine to soothe the child. Every parent and carer knows their child's sensory issues. Sometimes it is good to touch them, wrap them in a blanket, hold them close or sit them on your knee. However, touch and close physical contact can make other children much worse. Other well-tried soothing strategies include sitting quietly in a rocking chair or hammock, taking a warm bath or shower, or listening to quiet music through headphones.

SHARE THE DIAGNOSIS

The concern that professionals always raise about FASD is the stigma believed to be associated with diagnosis. This fear of stigma plus excessive concerns about confidentiality are the most common reasons given by professionals for not sharing the information with parents and carers. Affected children are the innocent victims of an invisible disability that is not their fault and they need to be surrounded by a community of people who understand them and their needs. Sharing the diagnosis with the extended family, friends and neighbours is the best starting point for ensuring that the child gets the support they need. It can also give adoptive parents more opportunities for short breaks because alcohol-damaged children, who are not obviously disabled, do not usually qualify for most local authority respite care services. Respite usually comes only from the extended family, and if they are kept in the dark they cannot help.

The child

All affected children know that they have a disability. They are often bewildered by the fact that they struggle with relatively simple tasks that their peers manage quite easily. Without age-appropriate information about the reasons for these daily struggles, the child can become progressively more anxious, depressed and isolated. When a child "owns" their disability and is clearly able to articulate it, the outcomes for them as adults will be more positive. Sharing the diagnosis with a child is not easy and it can be particularly heartbreaking for a birth mother. However, there are now a number of internet resources, books and computer apps for children, young people, their caregivers and friends. These materials, which are constantly being expanded and revised to cover various age groups, seek to explain in a straightforward way the implications of a FASD diagnosis.

The parents or carers

Many children who have been exposed to alcohol in pregnancy are not living with their birth families. The search for the right substitute family can be frustrating and time consuming. The social worker, who may have been involved in extended legal proceedings, can be understandably anxious for a vulnerable child to move quickly into a permanent placement. Whilst adoption is a process with many regulated checks and balances, when a child moves into a foster or kinship placement the process can move rapidly.

All carers will have undergone an assessment process and potentially endured a long wait. They can feel their lives have been "on hold" for months. In addition to the excitement of a child joining their family, parents or carers are often organising or renovating family homes, tying up loose ends at work in preparation for leave, or undertaking long journeys to the child's current family. Additional "soft" information, particularly in a healthy or very young child, may not seem a very important issue and many questions may be left unasked, only to be regretted later.

All carers need comprehensive and detailed knowledge about a child to parent sensitively and effectively. In addition to the usual roles that all parents undertake, substitute carers must *not* have to spend time uncovering, discovering or simply guessing about the past and its continuing influence on the future of their child. **No one should ever be asked to parent a child in the absence of all the information that is available to professionals.**

Unsurprisingly, another of Professor Streissguth's key findings is that children who are in the same placement or family for as long as possible have the best outcomes. Comprehensive identification and assessment of problems is likely to facilitate a placement rather than threaten it. Substitute carers require a very honest assessment of the difficulties that they are likely to face in meeting a child's needs. Only then can they help their child repair, rebuild or compensate for what has gone before. Only placement stability gives carers insight into a child's needs and a timeframe for coping strategies and support networks to develop.

The school

Although distracting and overstimulating environments such as large shopping centres at peak times are relatively easy to avoid, the school classroom with its humming fluorescent lights, visual displays, constant activity, complex social rules, constant verbal instructions and persistent background noise is the unavoidable place where all children must spend at least 11 years of their lives. Parents and carers who can manage their child in the protected, structured, supervised environment of their home are often shocked to find that school is a major challenge.

As they progress through school, children are expected to follow increasingly complex verbal instructions, plan independent work and solve problems based on instructions. Even the most able child with FASD will struggle with all these tasks. All affected children will find the abstract areas of the curriculum, particularly questions involving time, money and mathematics, very challenging. Schools are by their very nature less structured, less predictable and more distracting than home environments and most alcohol-affected children find it hard to concentrate in this environment. Finally, affected children will always struggle with the subtle but complex social rules of school life, particularly the older child approaching puberty.

Children with FASD may score within normal limits on measures of IQ, appear physically mature and give the appearance of functioning at a level consistent with their chronological age. Their expressive language may be in advance of their actual age, and their reading skills may be chronologically appropriate. However, the academic abilities of individuals with FASD are below their IQ level; their living skills, communication skills and adaptive behaviour levels are even further below IQ levels; and in areas such as social skills and emotional maturity, they may be performing at half of their developmental age (Streissguth *et al*, 1997). They need small group teaching, adapted environments like those provided for children with autism, clear and simple explanations, calming down strategies and help with understanding emotions and behaviour.

In the UK, teachers and educational psychologists are at an early stage in developing resources and educational support for FASD. Resources for the classroom include *Educating Children and Young People with Foetal Alcohol Spectrum Disorders* (Blackburn *et al*, 2012, Routledge), and will also be available from the UK FASD support groups listed in Appendix C. Most parents and carers have reported that their first role was that of educator to their child's school. They had to try to explain what FASD is, its effects on their child, and implications for learning and behaviour. Even among those who had a relatively positive experience with their child's school, there is still a need to advocate for their child. Avoiding the diagnosis or not telling the school because of stigma will not help the school to develop effective classroom support. Without this, children will almost certainly fail or be excluded from school.

Supervise, supervise, supervise

As a rule of thumb, children with FASD have a developmental age that is approximately half their chronological age. They are impulsive and lack self-control. They have trouble understanding the link between behaviour and consequences. They are immature, naïve, friendly and outgoing with little sense of stranger awareness. They are vulnerable to manipulation by older, more streetwise children and they are typically the child in any group who gets caught and blamed, even though they did not initiate or carry out the offending action. They need a level of supervision and parenting appropriate to their developmental age, not their chronological age, so that they do not get into serious trouble or place themselves in dangerous situations.

Parents and carers need to maintain a constant high level of supervision, even if they are accused of being over-protective and "not letting their child go". Parenting any young adult is very challenging and parenting the child with FASD is extra-challenging because FASD affects an individual's ability to live independently throughout their lives.

One major mistake often made by well-meaning professionals is the assumption that now the child is 17 or 18, they need to be "more independent". Parents should ignore this advice and social workers should never give it. When parents or carers, pressured by society's perception that all young people need to be given the freedom to be independent, have allowed their children out without adequate supervision, disaster soon follows.

The group most at risk are the alcohol-affected young adults looked after by a local authority who are expected to leave care with their peers and then manage alone with little additional support. Unfortunately, these young people are unsophisticated and lack the basic skills to cope with independent living. An affected child of 18 will have a developmental age of about nine. No parent would ever let a nine-year-old drive a car, go to a nightclub, stay out until the early hours of the morning or live alone, shop, cook and manage household bills.

Most adults with FASD will always need a lot of help to meet the more routine demands of work and home. Nearly 80 per cent of adults with FASD do not live independently. They will need help with employment, money management, housing, and social skills. Many require close daily supervision to help them make essential day-to-day decisions and keep themselves safe.

It is important to change society's focus from an exaggerated expectation of *independence* to one of life-long *interdependence*. A local supportive community is important for everyone, but it is essential for people with FASD. They need the "external brains" of the community around them to manage everyday life. They will always need a strong circle of support made up of family members, mentors, social workers, agency support workers, and others who understand the realities and limitations of FASD.

SUCCESS COMES IN SMALL UNEVEN STEPS

Parents and carers need to be patient and calm as well as having reduced and flexible expectations because, in the words of one parent, 'Things the child does well now he may not do well in two weeks' time'. There is very little that is slow and steady about children with FASD. Some days the child will show flashes of promising behaviour that exceed parental expectations. On these good days, a parent is tempted to think that their child does not have FASD or is only mildly affected. At the other extreme, on those days when the child falls short of already lowered expectations, it is easy to despair. The parent starts to imagine all the horror stories they have heard about living with FASD, a nightmare from which their family will never recover.

Inconsistent performance is very common in FASD. Occasionally, all children will meet or exceed parental expectations. Tragically, these fluctuations can reinforce the false belief that the child can do it "if only they try harder". In fact, the child is trying just as hard during an "on" day as on an "off" day and is frequently exhausted with trying and failing. Peaks and valleys in behaviour are normal in FASD. They are to be expected. They are not predictive of potential; they just are. When his family is struggling, one father always cites his favourite quote: 'When Plan A fails, remember there are still another 25 letters left in the alphabet'.

KNOWLEDGE IS POWER

Parents and carers who do not understand why their child is having so many difficulties doing and learning things that other children do easily are isolated and bewildered. They feel that their family and friends cannot understand what their daily life is like. Even worse, they can feel like a bad parent because other people in society, who do not understand FASD, blame them for their child's difficulties. To know that other parents are having similar problems is a great support.

Many parents and carers report that the first thing they did when they learned or suspected that they had a child with FASD was to educate themselves as much as they could. For them, education was a lifesaver, reducing their guilt and anxiety and has been a continuous process of discovery. All parents and carers should be encouraged to join, or even start, a support group and download some of the excellent resources available on the internet (see Appendices B and C).

KEY LEARNING POINT

Most teachers waste their time by asking questions that are intended to discover what a pupil does not know, whereas the true art of questioning is to discover what the pupil does know or is capable of knowing.

(Albert Einstein, 1920, from *Conversations with Albert Einstein*, Alexander Moszkowski, http://web.mit.edu/redingtn/www/netadv/ SP20140113.html)

Chapter 12
Dos and don'ts for social workers

'Please tell us exactly what to do' is a consistent request from all professionals in this field. Social workers are especially troubled by the topic of alcohol because they are working with children in care who have complex difficulties, who have been subject to multiple moves and their early history is often missing. In the absence of clear national guidelines, the following brief pointers may help.

Do remember that FASD is an incurable, lifelong disability that is also totally preventable. The number of affected individuals is unknown.

Do remember that whilst the prevalence of FASD in the care system is unknown, emerging evidence suggests that the numbers of affected children are much greater than in the general population. Social workers should become familiar with FASD and question, at the earliest possible opportunity, whether pre-birth alcohol consumption might play a part in the child's difficulties.

Do remember that services in the UK are at a very early stage of development. Experience from other countries suggests that the following will all be needed in the future (All Party Parliamentary Group on FASD, December 2015):

- universal preventive services to reduce the number of pregnancies affected by alcohol;
- guidelines for social and health care practitioners;
- pathways for the referral of individuals with suspected FASD to specialist clinics to allow a comprehensive diagnostic evaluation;
- specialist services to support and follow up those referrals;
- effective intervention programmes for families and schools;
- a comprehensive alcohol education programme across all agencies.

Do remember that at this early stage of service development, the onus will inevitably be on individual practitioners and their agencies to, firstly, reduce the number of women who drink alcohol in pregnancy; secondly, to increase their personal knowledge of FASD; and thirdly, to provide more effective support for the child and family. Affected individuals cannot wait for society to catch up with their needs.

Do remember the current guidance. The Chief Medical Officer recommends that if you are pregnant or planning to become pregnant, the safest approach is not to drink alcohol at all to keep risks to your baby to a minimum. Drinking in pregnancy can lead to long-term harm to the baby, with the more you drink, the greater the risk (January 2016).

Do remember that diagnostic services are still patchy across the UK and a "postcode lottery" operates. There is only one specialist national clinic. However, there are a small, but increasing number of paediatricians with an interest in FASD who are developing services in their local areas, and this situation will improve in the future.

Do not assume that diagnosis is purely a medical task – many different professionals are needed. The social worker, GP, health visitor, midwife and teacher all have a role to play.

Do remember a history of exposure to alcohol before birth is a vital component of diagnosis.

Do obtain, record and preserve information about a woman's lifestyle in pregnancy. This information must follow the child, who may not show symptoms for many years. Preserving the information is especially important for the child who may be taken into care and separated from their birth family history.

Do remember that alcohol and drug misuse coexist with other problems, and the following should all raise concern about the possibility of alcohol damage to an unborn child:

- a family history of alcohol misuse;

- a history of suicide attempts and self-harm;

- a history of neglect because alcohol dependence impairs parenting capacity;

- a history of domestic violence;

- a previous child with FASD.

Do not rely solely on facial features for diagnosis. These features are caused by exposure to alcohol in the first two months of pregnancy when the child's face is forming. If the mother does not drink alcohol in this period, the child's face will be normal. The majority of children damaged by prenatal alcohol exposure have no physical birth defects but will have the devastating cognitive and behavioural difficulties caused by alcohol exposure in the last three months of pregnancy.

Do remember that diagnosis matters. Diagnosis improves prognosis. Without it, children will be incorrectly diagnosed with other conditions, particularly ADHD, autism, an attachment or conduct disorder. Without diagnosis, inappropriate management techniques can be used, or ineffective medication prescribed.

Do remember that affected children can show very different patterns of strengths and difficulties because of the unpredictable nature of the damage to the frontal lobes of the brain.

Do not wait for a formal diagnosis to try strategies that have been shown to be effective in FASD, if that intervention works and helps the child.

Do not recommend traditional behaviour management strategies. They will fail with alcohol-affected children.

Do not ask anyone to provide substitute parenting (adoptive, foster or kinship) in the absence of all the information that is available to professionals. Comprehensive identification and assessment of problems is likely to facilitate a placement rather than threaten it. Substitute carers must not have to uncover, discover or simply guess about the past and its continuing influence on a child.

Do not assume that siblings should automatically be placed together. Alcohol-dependent women frequently have many children in quick succession. As her dependence on alcohol gets worse, the amount of alcohol the woman drinks increases and the children become progressively more damaged. The youngest child is usually the most severely affected. The children's needs become more complex and challenging as they get older and there is a limit to how many children and how many problems one family can manage.

Do not assume that young adults looked after by a local authority will be able to leave care with their peers and live independently. Nearly 80 per cent of adults with FASD do not live independently. They will need help with employment, money management, housing, and social skills. Many require close daily supervision to help them make essential day-to-day decisions and keep themselves safe.

Appendix A
Delivering an alcohol brief intervention

Stage 1 – Raise the issue

The next area for us to focus on is alcohol use. While some women go off alcohol when pregnant, many continue to have an occasional drink. Are you drinking at the moment?

Stage 2 – Screen and give feedback

Can you take me through what you normally drink in a week and on your heaviest drinking day during the week?

From what you've told me, you are drinking more than the current guidance for alcohol consumption during pregnancy…This means that the amount you are drinking is risky for your developing baby and also for your own health now and in the future.

Stage 3 – Listen for readiness to change

- *How do you feel about what we have discussed?*

- *What would be helpful to you just now?*

Stage 4 – Choose a suitable approach

Information and advice – on the impact of alcohol on her own health, and evidence for the impact of alcohol on the developing foetus, clarify the current national guidance on drinking while pregnant.

Enhance motivation – build the woman's motivation to change by helping her to weigh up the pros and cons of her drinking.

Menu of options – for changing drinking behaviour. Ask the woman if she can suggest ways to change her drinking pattern (e.g. lower alcoholic-strength drinks, having drink-free days, taking up other activities). Be ready to offer ideas if the woman agrees.

Build confidence – using an interviewing style that enhances the woman's belief in her ability to change, for example, identifying her previous successes and the role models she can learn from, and identifying other people who can support her.

Coping strategies – help the woman to identify times when she might find it more difficult to stick to her plans to cut down and to come up with strategies for coping with these situations.

(Taken from: NHS Health Scotland (2015) *Alcohol Brief Interventions: Antenatal professional pack*, Edinburgh: NHS Health Scotland, available at: www.healthscotland.scot/media/1281/antenatal-cribsheet_jan2017_english.pdf)

Appendix B
Guides for parents on FASD

Guides for parents (UK)

Foetal Alcohol Spectrum Disorder: Parenting a child with an invisible disability
Julia Brown and Dr Mary Mather, 2014
CreateSpace Independent Publishing Platform

Understanding Foetal Alcohol Spectrum Disorder
Maria Catterick and Liam Curran, 2014
Jessica Kingsley Publishers

Educating Children and Young People with Foetal Alcohol Spectrum Disorders
Carolyn Blackburn, Barry Carpenter and Jo Egerton, 2012
Routledge

Guides for parents (other countries)

Fantastic Antoine Succeeds: Experiences in educating children with FAS
Fantastic Antoine Grows Up: Experiences with adolescents and adults with FAS
Judith Kleinfeld and Siobhan Wescott, 1993 and 2000
University of Alaska Press

Supporting Caregivers of Children with Foetal Alcohol Spectrum Disorders
Anne Hedelius, 2012
CreateSpace Independent Publishing Platform

Strategies not Solutions
Edmonton and Area Fetal Alcohol Network, Alberta, Canada
Available as a PDF at: www.humanservices.alberta.ca/documents/
FAS0040-strategies-not-solutions.pdf

Appendix C
Support groups for parents and professionals

Support groups for parents and professionals (UK)

The following groups provide a range of services: information for families and communities, support groups for parents, training for families and practitioners, education for professionals, media campaigns for social change, and raising public awareness about the risks of alcohol consumption during pregnancy.

NOFAS UK
022 Southbank House
Black Prince Road
London SE1 7SJ
Helpline: 020 8458 5951
Email: help@nofas-uk.org or info@nofas-uk.org
www.nofas-uk.org

FASD Network UK
Tel: 07743 380163
Email: fasdnetwork@mail.com
www.fasdnetwork.org
Covers: North East England, Yorkshire and Humberside

FASD Trust
Unit 8, The Gallery
54 Marston Street
Oxford OX4 1LF
Tel: 01865 249771
Helpline: 01608 811599
Email: familysupport@fasdtrust.co.uk (For nearest family support group)
www.fasdtrust.co.uk
www.fasdineducation.co.uk. (educational support and teacher training)

FASD Scotland
Email: info@fasdscotland.com
www.fasdscotland.com

FASD UK Alliance
Email: fasd-uk@live.com
https://fasd-uk.net/

A coalition of groups and individuals from across the UK including small local, regional and virtual groups as well as some of the country's longest-standing national organisations devoted to FASD. Their Facebook Support Group connects more than 1,100 birth parents, foster carers, adopters, extended families and adults with FASD. Within this closed group, members can share information and ask questions. The group's resources pages include useful documents and publications and links to international networks.

UK and European Birth Mum Network – FASD
Tel: 020 7692 1695
Email: eurobmsngroup@yahoo.com
www.eurobmsn.org/home.html

Affiliated with the FASD UK Alliance. A network of women who may have a child or children with FASD. The network is a place where women can share their experiences, support each other and provide peer support for women and their families. The aim is to help prevent FASD by raising awareness, educating, and increasing understanding for birth mothers and their families.

National Clinic for Fetal Alcohol Spectrum Disorder
The UK's only specialist national FASD clinic. Specialises in assessing and treating children and adults with FASD.

Surrey and Borders Partnership NHS Trust
Gatton Place
St Matthews Road
Redhill
RH1 1TA
Tel: 01737 288813
www.fasdclinic.com/

Support groups for parents and professionals (international)

These websites are useful because these countries have had services for affected children and their families for many years. Although not designed specifically for a UK audience, they contain a lot of practical information, help and advice for parents.

National Organization on Fetal Alcohol Syndrome USA
www.nofas.org

Directory of Fetal Alcohol Spectrum Disorder (FASD) Information and Support Services in Canada
www.faslink.org/ccsa_Directory_2005.pdf

National Organization on Fetal Alcohol Syndrome Australia
www.nofasd.org.au/resources/fasd-support-groups

Appendix D
Calculating the units in alcoholic drinks

Alcohol units – Live Well – NHS Choices

www.nhs.uk/Livewell/alcohol/Pages/alcohol-units.aspx

Unit and Calorie Calculator – Drinkaware

www.drinkaware.co.uk/understand-your-drinking/unit-calculator

What is an alcohol unit? – Drinkaware

www.drinkaware.co.uk/alcohol-facts/alcoholic-drinks-units/what-is-an-alcohol-unit/

BMJ Best Practice: Foetal Alcohol Spectrum Disorders – British Medical Journal

http://bestpractice.bmj.com/topics/en-gb/1141?locale=it&

Appendix E
Professional guides to diagnosis

UK

British Medical Association (2016) *Foetal Alcohol Spectrum Disorders: A guide for healthcare practitioners update*, London: BMA Board of Science

Canada

Cook J, Green C, Lilley C, Anderson S, Baldwin M, Chudley A, Conry JL, LeBlanc N, Locock C, Lutke J, Mallon B, McFarlane A, Temple V and Rosales T (2016) *Fetal Alcohol Spectrum Disorder: A guideline for diagnosis across the lifespan,* Canada Fetal Alcohol Spectrum Disorder Research Network

USA

National Center on Birth Defects and Developmental Disabilities, Centers for Disease Control and Prevention, Department of Health and Human Services with National Task Force on Fetal Alcohol Syndrome and Fetal Alcohol Effect (2005) *Fetal Alcohol Syndrome: Guidelines for referral and diagnosis*, available at: www.cdc.gov/ncbddd/fasd/documents/FAS_guidelines_accessible.pdf

Australia

Bower C and Elliot EJ on behalf of the Steering Group (2016) *Report to the Australian Government Department of Health: Australian guide to the diagnosis of foetal alcohol spectrum disorder (FASD)*, University of Sydney, available at: www.apsu.org.au/assets/Uploads/20160505-rep-australian-guide-to-diagnosis-of-fasd.pdf

References

Alberta Alcohol and Drug Abuse Commission (2006) *Women Working Toward their Goals through AADAC Enhanced Services for Women*, Alberta: Alberta Health Services

All-Party Parliamentary Group for FASD (2015) *Initial Report of the Inquiry into the Current Picture of FASD in the UK Today*, available at: www.appg-fasd.org.uk/reports/4589489444

British Medical Association (2016) 'Foetal Alcohol Spectrum Disorders: a guide for healthcare practitioners update', London: BMA Board of Science

Chan AKW, Pristach EA, Welte JW and Russell M (1993) 'Use of the TWEAK test in screening for alcoholism/heavy drinking in three populations', *Alcoholism: Clinical and Experimental Research*, 17, pp.1188–92

Department of Health, Welsh Government, Department of Health Northern Ireland and Scottish Government (2016) UK Chief Medical Officers' Low Risk Drinking Guidelines, available at: www.gov.uk/government/uploads/system/uploads/attachment_data/file/545937/UK_CMOs__report.pdf

Frank D, Debenedetti AF, Volk RJ, Williams E, Kivlahan D and Bradley K (2008) 'Effectiveness of the AUDIT-C as a screening test for alcohol misuse in three race/ethnic groups', *Journal of General Internal Medicine*, 23:6, pp.781–787

Gregory G, Reddy V and Young C (2015) 'Identifying children who are at risk of FASD in Peterborough: working in a community clinic without access to gold standard dignosis', *Adoption & Fostering*, 39:3, pp.225–234

Health and Social Care Information Centre (2012) *Household Survey England 2011*, Leeds: Health and Social Care Information Centre

Health and Social Care Information Centre (2013) *Statistics on Alcohol: England 2013*, Leeds: Health and Social Care Information Centre

Jones KL and Smith DW (1973) 'Recognition of the foetal alcohol syndrome in early infancy', *The Lancet*, 2, pp.999–1001

Lemoine P, Harousseau H, Borteyru JP and Menuet JC (1968) 'Les enfants de parents alcooliques: anomalies observées à propos de 127 cas', *Ouest Med*, 21, pp.476–482

Mather M (2015) 'Editorial: the invisible disability', *Adoption & Fostering*, 39:3, pp.197–200

Mather M, Wiles K and O'Brien P (2015) 'Head to head: should women abstain from alcohol throughout pregnancy?', *British Medical Journal*, 351: h5232

Mattson SN, Schoenfeld AM and Riley EP (2001) *Teratogenic Effects of Alcohol on Brain and Behaviour*, National Institute on Alcohol and Alcoholism, USA Department of Health, available at: https://pubs.niaaa.nih.gov/publications/arh25-3/185-191.htm

Motz M, Leslie M, Pepler DJ, Moore T and Freeman P (2006) *Breaking the Cycle: Measures of progress 1995–2005 – Journal of FAS International,* 4, pp.e22

Mukherjee R, Cook PJ, Flemming KN and Norgate SH (2017) 'What can be done to lessen morbidity associated with foetal alcohol spectrum disorders?', *Archives of Diseases in Childhood*, 102, pp.463–467

Mukherjee R, Wray E, Curfs, L and Hollins S (2013) 'Estimation of alcohol content of wine, beer and spirits to evaluate exposure risk in pregnancy: pilot study using a questionnaire and pouring task in England', *International Journal of Alcohol and Drug Research*, 2:3, pp.71–78

Nykjaer C, Alwan NA, Greenwood DC, Simpson N, Hay A, White K and Cade J (2014) 'Maternal alcohol intake prior to and during pregnancy and risk of adverse birth outcomes: evidence from a British cohort', *Journal of Epidemiology and Community Health*, 0:1–8, doi:10.1136/jech-2013-202934

Phillips WA (2015) 'Prenatal exposure to alcohol causes enduring brain damage', *Adoption & Fostering*, 39:3, pp.201–211

Popova S, Lange S, Probst C, Gmel G and Rehm J (2017) 'Estimation of national, regional and global prevalence of alcohol use during pregnancy and foetal alcohol syndrome: a systematic review and meta-analysis', *The Lancet Global Health*, 5:6, pp.e575–e576

Preece P and Riley EP (eds) (2011) *Alcohol, Drugs and Medication in Pregnancy*: *The long-term outcome for the child*, Clinics in Developmental Medicine 188, MacKeith Press: London

Selwyn J and Wijedesa D (2011) 'Pathways to adoption for minority children in England', *Child and Family Social Work*, 16, pp.276–286

Shen D (2012) *Statistical Handbook 2012, British Beer and Pub Association*, London: Brewing Publications Ltd

Sokol RJ, Martier SS and Ager JW (1989) 'The T-ACE questions: practical prenatal detection of risk drinking', *American Journal of Obstetrics and Gynaecology*, 160, pp.863–8

Standage T (2005) *A History of the World in Six Glasses*, Walker Publishing Company: USA

Stratton K, Howe C and Battaglia F (eds) (1996) *Foetal Alcohol Syndrome: Diagnosis, epidemiology, prevention, and treatment*, Washington DC: National Academy Press

Streissguth A, Barr H, Kogan J and Bookstein F (1997) 'Primary and secondary disabilities in foetal alcohol syndrome, in Streissguth AP and Kanter J (eds) *The Challenge of Foetal Alcohol Syndrome: Overcoming secondary disabilities*, Seattle: University of Washington Press, pp.25–39

Streissguth AP, Landesman-Dwyer S, Martin JC and Smith DW (1980) 'Teratogenic effects of alcohol in humans and laboratory animals', *Science*, 209:4454, pp.353–361

Streissguth AP and O'Malley KD (2000) 'Neuropsychiatric implications and long-term consequences of foetal alcohol spectrum disorders', *Seminars in Clinical Neuropsychiatry*, 5, pp.177–190

Sullivan WC (2011) 'A note on the influence of maternal inebriety on the offspring', *Journal of Mental Science*, 1899:45, pp.489–503) reprinted *International Journal of Epidemiology*, 2011:40, pp.278–82

US Surgeon General (2005) *US Surgeon General releases advisory on alcohol use in pregnancy*, 21 February, available at: http://come-over.to/FAS/SurGenAdvisory.htm

Warner RH and Rosett HL (1975) 'The effects of drinking on offspring: an historical survey of the American and British literature', *Journal of Studies on Alcohol and Drugs*, 36, pp.1395–402

PARENTING MATTERS

This unique series provides expert knowledge about a range of children's health conditions, coupled with facts, figures and guidance presented in a straightforward and accessible style. Adopters and foster carers also describe what it is like to parent an affected child, "telling it like it is", sharing their parenting experiences and offering useful advice.

To find out more visit www.corambaaf.org.uk/bookshop